FEEL BETTER!

LIVE LONGER!

RELAX

To Mary, whose love and advice have both

been so helpful.

FEEL BETTER! LIVE LONGER! RELAX

by

Richard L. Lutz

DIMI PRESS
Salem, Oregon

Library of Congress Cataloging in Publication Data
Lutz, Richard L., 1929——
Feel Better! : live longer! : relax.
        Bibliography: p
        Includes index
            1. Relaxation——Health aspects.   I. Title.
RA785.L872   1988   613.7'9   88—10872
ISBN: 0-931625-18-1 (pbk.)
DIMI PRESS
3820 Oak Hollow Lane, SE
Salem, Oregon 97302
Printed in the United States of America
First Edition, Second Printing

TABLE OF CONTENTS

ACKNOWLEDGMENTS

Thanks are due those who helped me learn the techniques outlined in this book. Karen Coville, RN and Donna Cohara, among others,allowed me to use them as 'guinea pigs' from the very first. Ann Nelson, MSW, and Dr. Clem Vickery, consulting psychiatrist, encouraged me in my independent learning at the beginning. Steve Summers, attorney, also helped with legal questions in the compiling of this book. Ann Fuji, RD, provided some of the information for the WEIGHT CONTROL script.

Perhaps most important are the many clients (who, for obvious reasons, must remain anonymous) of the West Salem Clinic. These good people trustingly allowed me to hone my skills on them and also provided me with the encouragement to go on using relaxation as a technique for treatment/improvement.

During my research on relaxation at the West Salem Clinic, I was beginning an independent practice of psychotherapy. Relaxation proved a very useful treatment technique with private clients as well. I owe a debt to them, also.

In shaping up the manuscript of this book, I am grateful to Dr. Jim King, an excellent therapist and teacher of relaxation techniques, for reading and commenting so helpfully on my 'first born'.

To my daughter, Judy Lutz, for the outstanding job of editing the manuscript.

Thanks are also due to Sharon Schnare for designing the cover.

Lastly, my gratitude to Rick Goldman for suggesting the title.

FOREWORD

THE JOY OF DEEP REST — One of the nicest aspects of a good experience is to be able to share that experience with others. If we have a good meal at a new and different restaurant, we look forward to telling friends of our new find. In retelling the experience, we again dip into the stored pleasures tucked away inside us. Relaxation can be such a pleasure to share.

Dick Lutz has shared a variety of menus that can be savored and enjoyed in this most pleasant state of life. You can choose a fine meal composed of deep muscle release. The rush of tightened muscles as they release tension shoots pulsating warmth that radiates and soaks every fiber of sensation. The whole body is flooded with a surge of pleasure like a wave crashing on the shore to finally experience peace, stillness and total absorption.

With advancing skill, you can be a gourmet of consciousness and choose to "travel" to the beautiful imagery spot of your choosing. In this self-conjured setting you can create, if you like, the orange capped, purple mountains framed by a red sky surrounded by deep blue trees among tall, lavender grass. It can be a quiet place, a secret place that only you visit; a place to be still and fully absorbed in the wonders of your mind.

The marvelous aspect of this skill called meditation, relaxation, stress reduction or self-hypnosis is that it is really very good for you. In a state of deep relaxation you can heal the wounds of life's daily battle to survive. Your body literally soaks up the much needed rest. Body fluids flow freely like a rain storm on the parched desert sands. You live longer and healthier because you release the pressure, allowing the engines to cool down.

Your breathing is cool and refreshing. Your mind is no longer twisted and contorted by the crazed, mazed script describing your life. Your thoughts are free. Like a big gulp of air after being submerged, your mind draws in the cool refreshment in states of deep relaxation like Theta and Delta brainwaves. Colors may dance before your eyes. You might get swept away in a full blown vision or vivid dream that can be so real you forget your body is sitting quietly and resting.

The restorative quality of deep rest repairs the damage of our self-abusive way of living. Blood pressure can be returned to safer and life extending levels. Mind smashing headaches will no longer reign supreme as haunting specters waiting to emerge and rule our every move. Vital organs like the liver can restore themselves and thus stabilize our energy level. We can rise and feel after 30 minutes of deep rest as if we had a two to three hour Sunday nap. Unfortunately, no one has ever trained us to control our bodies in this fashion. As a culture we wait until people have damaged themselves and their life is impaired or threatened before we encourage them to take care of themselves. Children learn these skills very quickly and that is certainly where this training should start. If you are an adult and if your life has been stressful for quite a number of years, be sure and give yourself time to learn this new skill.

In addition to learning to relax, you will also be working at releasing those years of stored pressure. The experience may not be pleasant as that old stress garbage is unloaded. Be patient. Treat yourself as an infant struggling to move. Then crawl. And finally walk. Most of all enjoy the feeling. Just for once, DON'T WORRY.

In a state of deep rest you will be in good company. Many individuals have spent entire lifetimes mastering these basic skills. Be glad that you have undertaken this journey with this first step. Each step will flow upon the other as you journey into a land filled with refreshment and wonder. ENJOY!

November, 1987   Timothy J. Lowenstein, Ph.D.
                               Director, CONSCIOUS
                               LIVING
                               FOUNDATION

PREFACE

In 1980 I went to work as a mental health counselor at a medical clinic. It so happened that the clinic had ordered some biofeedback equipment and it had arrived before I had a caseload. Since I didn't have much else to do, I began experimenting with biofeedback as a treatment technique. First with staff and then with patients, I read relaxation narrations to people while they were hooked up to the biofeedback instrument. The changes in temperature and/or nervous tension that regularly occurred were remarkable, but it became clear to me that the real benefit came from the relaxation narration itself. It had profound beneficial effects for almost everyone I tested, not just those patients whose emotional problems I was working to relieve.

Since my wife had long commented that my reading to her put her to sleep, I decided to narrate a relaxation narration on cassette tape. To avoid copyright problems, I wrote my own narrations and proceeded to record them.

From there, I progressed to making a number of relaxation tapes, which proved popular enough to encourage me to put several of them into an album. In the following years, I became increasingly convinced of the efficacy of relaxation narrations for everyone.

By writing and publishing this book, I hope to reach a larger number of people who can benefit from the use of relaxation narrations. In the future I am sure I will continue my efforts to learn more about relaxation and to bring that information to the attention of the public.

September, 1987

Dick Lutz
Salem, Oregon

INTRODUCTION

According to a Louis Harris poll, 89% of all adult Americans report experiencing high stress. Fifty-nine per cent of adult Americans say they feel "great stress" at least once or twice a week, while 30% report living with high stress nearly every day. Stress is a significant factor in the lives of most people.

This book does not deal extensively with theories of stress, but rather with practical ways of controlling it. Thus, the Harris figures on the percentages of people who use different techniques to control their stress (or relieve their suffering) are fascinating.

His research finds that three out of every ten people who suffer from stress do nothing to control it. Of those who do something, the researcher says they take three main steps: 1) prepare themselves mentally; 2) take physical steps to relieve it; or 3) alter their social behavior to avoid stressful situations.

The use of relaxation in the handling of stress can be considered both a mental and physical step, so perhaps a large number of people already practice relaxation techniques. Unfortunately, my experience indicates this is not the case. Apparently only a minority of adults practice relaxation techniques of any kind.

The reasons for this include a certain self-consciousness, a lack of knowledge of the effectiveness of these techniques, and a lack of know-how about the best technique to use. It is my hope that this book demonstrates the effectiveness of relaxation as well as describing some of the methods to be used. Actually doing the relaxation narration will rapidly overcome any self-consciousness.

The theme of this book is not simply the use of relaxation in the handling of stress, important as that is. An enumeration of the problems that can be successfully addressed through the use of relaxation is also included. While I am aware that I do not yet know all of the beneficial uses of relaxation, I invite you to let me know as you discover additional benefits not covered in this book.

The Importance of Relaxing

1. The Importance of Relaxing

"The claims of any manual on relaxation must be modestly stated. "
Dr. Edmund Jacobson

In keeping with Dr. Jacobson's injunction, I do not wish to make grandiose claims for the benefits of relaxation. However, some well-proven accomplishments have been: the control of migraine headaches, the lowering of high blood pressure, the treatment of Raynaud's Syndrome, the alleviation of cardiovascular complaints, the lessening of chronic pain and tension headaches, the reduction of pain from rheumatoid arthritis, the control of allergies and asthma, the diminishing of abdominal disorders, the elimination of insomnia, and the ability to deal with anxiety, depression, and phobias. Not yet as well documented is the use of relaxation in dealing with the problems of shyness, premature ejaculation, and cancer. Relaxation is also routinely done to assist with habit changes such as losing weight and quitting smoking.

Perhaps these claims seem to the average reader of this book to be exaggerated but actually they are not. It is important to remember, though, that relaxation is not always successful in treating these conditions. But then, is anything dealing with human beings effective 100% of the time?

FEEL BETTER! LIVE LONGER! RELAX

Relaxation is extremely important in living a long, healthy life. It is a way for the body to 'recharge its batteries' and to be ready to cope with internal or external stressors. According to the dictionary, the verb 'to relax' is defined as "to make or become less firm, tense, severe, etc." As applied to the human body this means that the muscles must become less firm and tense. The process of making your muscles relax is a skill that you can (and will) learn from reading this book. Listening to the narration on a cassette (whether you make it yourself or buy a prerecorded narration) will also assist you in learning how to relax your muscles and, consequently, your body.

Stress and relaxation may be considered opposites. In medical terminology, anything which causes stress is known as a 'stressor'. A stressor, then, is the enemy of relaxation. It has been said that all stress is within ourselves, implying that if we did not react to stressors we would all be relaxed all of the time. Although probably true, this theory fails to take into account two facts:

First, we are all human. We react to stressors by becoming stressed. As we all know, human beings are not perfect.

Second, through the course of evolution, humans developed what Dr. Walter Cannon identified over 50 years ago as the 'fight or flight' response. This is a physiological reaction in which the presentation of danger (or the sudden appear-

The Importance of Relaxing

ance of an external stressor) results in a variety of bodily changes that prepare the human animal to fight or flee the danger presented. The bodily changes are described as follows by L. John Mason in his book GUIDE TO STRESS REDUCTION:

1. The heartbeat increases to pump blood throughout the body with greater speed, carrying oxygen and nutrients to cells and clearing away waste products more quickly.

2. As the heart rate increases, the blood pressure rises.

3. Breathing becomes rapid and shallow.

4. Adrenaline and other hormones are released into the blood.

5. The liver releases stored sugar into the blood, providing the body with extra energy.

6. The pupils dilate to let in more light; all the senses are heightened.

7. Muscles tense for movement, either for flight or for protective actions, particularly the skeletal muscles of the thighs, hips, back, shoulders, arms, jaw, and face.

8. Blood flow is greatly constricted to the digestive organs.

9. Blood flow increases to the brain and major muscles.

10. Blood flow to the extremities is constricted, and the hands and feet become cold. This protects a person from bleeding to death quickly if the hands or feet are injured while the person is fighting or fleeing. It also allows blood to be diverted to areas of the body (like the brain and muscles) that need it more.

11. The body perspires to cool itself, since the increased activity generates more heat.

The above constitutes a description of the body's automatic responses to an external stressor. There are also internal stressors. The reaction of the body to internal and external stressors is identical. Some examples of internal stressors are worry about bills, concern about job future, and anxiety about physical health. External stressors would be things like the flat tire you get while on the freeway, the sudden blackness in your living room in the evening when the electricity goes off, or the shrill ring of your alarm clock when you are in a deep sleep. These are only a few examples of the internal or external stressors to which civilization exposes us. The tiger in the jungle has been replaced by rush hour traffic, but the human body still responds to the stressors in the same way. The techniques of relaxation taught in this book should prove ideal in helping you to cope with both types of stressors.

Since 1929, it has been possible for doctors to chart brain

The Importance of Relaxing

waves and determine the level of relaxation in their patients. The electroencephalogram (EEG), also called the brain-wave test, measures in microvolts and in cycles per second (or Hertz) the extremely small electrical charge that constantly pulses from the human brain. Wires attached to the patient's scalp transmit the electrical charge to needles which in turn record the brain waves on a graph attached to a revolving drum. Like a seismograph recording earthquake activity, the needles jiggling on the drum report the fluctuating levels of electricity in the charge from the brain. The number of times per second that the marks go back and forth indicate the cycles per second. It is the latter with which we are concerned.

The patterns found in the recorded brain waves have been divided into four categories according to their cycles per second. The four are named and described below:

1. Beta (14-30 cycles per second)

2. Alpha (8-13 cycles per second)

3. Theta (4-7 cycles per second)

4. Delta (1-3 cycles per second)

The Beta waves are indicative of a state of mental alertness and quiet thought. The Theta and Delta stages represent sleep, with Theta waves being characteristic of early sleep while Delta waves show a deep sleep. The Alpha stage

FEEL BETTER! LIVE LONGER! RELAX

occurs when a person's brain is relaxed but awake. In most cases, when the EEG records Alpha waves the patient is deeply relaxed. Through the EEG wires, the brain itself can tell a doctor when the patient is relaxed.

A second objective measure of relaxation is the measurement of skin temperature. With some exceptions, the warmer the skin temperature the more relaxed the person inside the skin. Skin temperature is affected by body temperature (which is almost constant in a healthy person), the outside air temperature, and the amount of blood circulating under the skin. We can have little, if any, effect on our body temperature. Air temperature can, in most circumstances, be controlled to some extent. Other factors being equal, we feel more relaxed in a warm room than in a cold room. As will be discussed in more detail in the section on biofeedback, blood circulation can be affected by thinking.

As we achieve a greater depth of relaxation the warmth of our skin increases. Conversely, as we increase the warmth of our skin (particularly through increased circulation) we are more relaxed. I suppose it would be possible to get into a "which came first - the chicken or the egg" argument about whether the increased circulation causes the relaxation or whether the relaxation causes the increased circulation. But the only important point is that the amount of relaxation can be measured by the increase in skin temperature.

For those who are interested, there are a number of

The Importance of Relaxing

thermometers on the market for measuring skin temperature. These thermometers come in a wide range of complexity (and expensiveness).

The tension of the muscles can also be measured and an indication of the depth of relaxation obtained in this manner. The device used in measuring muscle relaxation is called an electromyogram and has long been familiar in doctors' offices. It measures the electrical discharge produced when muscles contract. When electrodes are attached to the skin the amount of electrical discharge in the muscles immediately under the skin is measured and can be recorded. This provides a rough measure of relaxation.

Although relaxation is generally thought of as a subjective experience, we have seen that there are at least three methods of objectively measuring it. For the purist, it should be admitted that these methods are frequently uneven in their results and sometimes don't work at all. However, research on most of these techniques is still at an early stage.

It has long been known that many athletes (professional, Olympic, and others) make use of relaxation techniques to enhance their performance. In most cases it works. VISUALIZATION (one of the relaxation techniques to be described later in this book) is perhaps the technique most commonly used by athletes but it is more frequently used to visualize succeeding in a planned endeavor rather than simply for relaxation. Still, here's what Joe Namath, the former quarterback for the New York Jets, had to say about the relaxation

FEEL BETTER! LIVE LONGER! RELAX

procedure called TRANSCENDENTAL MEDITATION:

"I started the Transcendental Meditation program because I felt like I wasn't doing anything for myself, for the growth of my system. I was wasting time. I wasn't reading, wasn't doing anything, wasn't really growing. So I started meditating because of the effects it has on your body and your mind, and it's done a great deal. It's made me feel like I am helping myself and through that I can get along with other people and maybe help them a little more with different situations or problems. The main thing though, I feel like it's helping me, and that in itself has done so much for my whole togetherness. I feel like I'm not wasting myself, that I am helping my mind and my body live life in the right way. And I've enjoyed it and I'm going to keep on enjoying it."

Others use relaxation as a means of releasing their potential, enhancing their creativity, or increasing their productivity. Also speaking of Transcendental Meditation (TM), Major General Franklin M. Davis, Commandant, U.S. War College, said:

"My blood pressure went down ten points. My wife said my disposition improved, and minor stresses and strains of life around Washington didn't bother me any more."

The psychological tests covering the area of relaxation seem to cover stress more than relaxation. It is perhaps true that psychological tests, like physical tests, tend to

The Importance of Relaxing

measure negative things more than positive things. Tests can be useful in assessing stress. Many individuals are unaware of the fact that they are stressed and that this stress is affecting their lives. These are the individuals who can benefit from tests that measure psychological stress.

Dr. Leonard R. Derogatis, in his paper "Self-report Measures of Stress" in HANDBOOK OF STRESS lists a number of these tests, including the Minnesota Multiphasic Personality Inventory (MMPI), a measure frequently used by stress researchers. Another very sensitive test is the SCL-90-R. According to Derogatis, the Beck Depression Inventory is broadly used to measure stress and distress associated with psychological disorders. The State-Trait Anxiety Inventory (STAI) provides a distinction between anxiety as a permanent personality characteristic— 'trait anxiety'— and anxiety as a temporary emotional experience— 'state anxiety'. A rather brief and simple-to-administer scale is the Self-rating Anxiety Scale (SAS). The Jenkins Activity Survey (JAS) is designed to measure Type A behavior, which is discussed in Chapter 2 of this book. Derogatis also discusses his own test, the Derogatis Stress Profile (DSP). In the conclusion of his article Derogatis quotes Hinkle as arguing that the concept of stress has acquired so many excess meanings that it is not too helpful in predicting the onset of disease. Hinkle's point shows the scientific community's interest in finding ways to assess as well as treat stress.

As we go on to talk about the various methods of relaxation (particularly in Chapter 3), it must be remem-

FEEL BETTER! LIVE LONGER! RELAX

bered that people vary a great deal. Some people are better 'relaxers' than others and most will find that a single relaxation technique works best for them.

One predictor of how easily a person will learn relaxation is the amount of experience a person has had in the same or another relaxation technique. Not only the amount but (perhaps more importantly) the positive nature of that experience is very significant. For example, when a person comes into my office for the purpose of learning to relax and reveals that she has been through a Yoga class and enjoyed it, I am confident that she will pick up any technique I teach her in short order. Anybody who has a philosophical belief in 'mind over matter' is way ahead on learning a relaxation technique.

One negative indication is the client who, metaphorically speaking, sees everything in black or white, but seldom gray. This type of thinking does not lend itself to the subtle, intuitive, in-touch-with-oneself inner feeling that is required for deep relaxation. As will be seen later, the muscle relaxation techniques require less of this abstract quality than do the mind relaxation techniques.

Another negative sign, which can usually be overcome, is a person's inordinate amount of anxiety about the procedure itself. Some anxiety is normal whenever we do something for the first time, particularly when that something is going to make us feel different. This is a frequent problem with hypnosis, in particular. A fear of hypnosis has been common in our society for centuries. Although scientists and doctors

The Importance of Relaxing

have stressed time and again that these fears are groundless, these statements have not made the anxiety disappear. If you are somewhat anxious or self-conscious about the mind relaxation techniques, you'll probably do better starting with a muscle relaxation technique.

FEEL BETTER! LIVE LONGER! RELAX

Theories of Relaxation

---

2. Theories of Relaxation

Perhaps the first recorded references to relaxation (though that term was not used) are the accounts of ancient Egyptian sleep temples. As near as we can tell these were places where what we now call hypnosis took place.

Benson, in THE RELAXATION RESPONSE, quotes several writings by early religious writers that deal in one way or another with relaxation. Although Benson focuses only on meditation and this book describes a number of relaxation techniques, his references are instructive.

Perhaps the earliest Christian writer to deal with this subject was St. Augustine (A.D. 354-430). One of his topics was what he referred to as 'contemplation', which had as its end point direct union with God. St. Augustine described preparation for contemplation as 'recollection', which Benson feels corresponds to a passive attitude — one of the four essential elements of Benson's method and also an important component of all other relaxation techniques. In Benson's words, "Recollection is an exercise of abstraction, of recollecting and gathering together thoughts ('memory') and concentrating the mind. The object is to shut off the mind from external thoughts and to produce a mental solitude."

Later, in about the fourteenth century, an anonymous monk wrote a book called THE CLOUD OF UNKNOWING in which he discussed the handling of distractions to contemplation: "Try to cover these thoughts with a thick cloud of forgetting as though they never existed neither for you nor for any other man. And if they continue to arise, continue to put them down." He also advises that his readers can develop "special ways, tricks, private techniques, and spiritual devices" in order to achieve contemplation. A specific device he refers to is the use of a one syllable word for "dwelling upon". This, too, is one of Benson's four essential elements, but it is not used in the other relaxation techniques. The anonymous monk suggested the use of a single syllable such as "God" or "love"" for dwelling upon, or:

"Choose whichever one you prefer, or if you like, choose another that suits your tastes, provided that it is of one syllable. And clasp this word tightly in your heart so that it never leaves it no matter what may happen. This word shall be your shield and your spear whether you ride in peace or in war. With this word you shall beat upon the cloud and the darkness, which are above you. With this word you shall strike down thoughts of every kind and drive them beneath the cloud of forgetting."

In the sixteenth century, Martin Luther wrote of a method for preparing for prayer. He recommends dwelling upon an object in order to prevent thoughts from intruding. For that object Luther proposes the words of the Lord's Prayer, the Ten Commandments, the Psalms, or one of a number of the sayings by Christ and Paul.

Theories of Relaxation

A sixteenth-century monk, Fray Francisco de Osuna, also wrote down some guidelines for contemplation:

"Although these practices and others of the same kind are excellent, our Letter advises those who wish to make further progress and follow better things to accustom themselves to recollection, for they will imitate and follow the Lord, whose custom it was to go into the desert, where, alone and recollected, he could pray more secretly and spiritually to his and our heavenly Father."

St. Teresa was greatly influenced by Fray Francisco's writings and wrote further about contemplation:

"... so the soul raises herself to a loftier region; she withdraws her senses from exterior objects ... those who adopt this method almost always pray with their eyes shut ... because it is making an effort not to think about earthly things."

Similarly, shutting your eyes is recommended in all methods of relaxation taught in this book and withdrawing your senses from exterior objects is also an integral part of relaxation.

Thus we have seen that early Christian writings include instructions that are amazingly similar to those in this book. The closeness between their instructions for prayer and the instructions given here for relaxation is striking. It is obvious (and my experience demonstrates it) that the individual who has a well-developed prayer life finds it very easy to relax themselves. These comments are not intended to diminish the importance of the religious aspect of prayer, but simply to point out the parallels between prayer and relaxation. Not only has the Christian faith developed a body of literature on 'how to relax' (though of course that is not its sole aim), but other religions have also.

The Jewish religion has a tradition of what is called 'mysticism' describing various meditative techniques. In one technique the meditator put his head between his knees, whispered hymns, and repeated the name of a magic emblem. According to one scholar of Jewish mysticism, Gershom G. Scholem, this enabled the person to reach "an attitude of deep self-oblivion". That phrase might well describe what any person using a relaxation technique attempts to achieve.

Permeating all Eastern religions is Yoga, which might be described as a philosophy as well as a discipline. Yoga meditation can be considered the ultimate relaxation technique.The lessons that Western science has learned from Yoga have been extremely valuable in the development of many of the relaxation techniques described in this book.

While the history of relaxation would fill another book, this brief chronology lists the known highlights in relaxation's development from a mystic practice to the

Theories of Relaxation

scientifically documented technique it is today.

IMPORTANT DATES IN THE HISTORY OF RELAXATION

3000 B.C.(?) - Egyptian sleep temples, the first recorded use of what is now known as hypnosis.

1400 A.D.(?) - First known 'instructions' in relaxation techniques.

1779 - Anton Mesmer's MEMOIRS published. The book spelled out the development of mesmerism, which is now called hypnotism and is a major method of relaxation.

1841 - Dr. James Braid's study of mesmerism begun. Later, he coined the term 'hypnotism'.

1845 - Hypnotism used extensively in surgery in India. This was the first quantitative proof that relaxation could be used to reduce or eliminate the sensation of pain.

1920(?) - Relaxation narration recorded on a phonograph record for the first time.

1929 - Dr. Edmund Jacobson's PROGRESSIVE RELAXA TION published.

FEEL BETTER! LIVE LONGER! RELAX

1932 - Dr. J.H. Schultz's AUTOGENIC TRAINING, CONCENTRATIVE SELF-RELAXATION published.

1950 - Relaxation narration recorded on an audio cassette for the first time.

1956 - Dr. Hans Selye's THE STRESS OF LIFE published. This classic work presented the concept of 'stress' in modern life as analogous to the 'stress' in physical matter.

1959 - Transcendental Meditation introduced to the United States by Maharishi Mahesh Yogi.

1974 - Dr. Meyer Friedman and Dr. Ray H. Rosenman's TYPE A BEHAVIOR AND YOUR HEART published. This landmark book introduced a new phrase, 'Type A Behav ior', into the English language.

1975 - Dr. Herbert Benson's THE RELAXATION RESPONSE published.

1980(?) - Relaxation narration recorded on a video cassette for the first time.

1982 - Computer used to enhance biofeedback for the first time.

Perhaps this is the place to discuss a very important

Theories of Relaxation

concept. Dr. Hans Selye talked about the value of stress in our lives. This is important because many of us who are aware of the benefits of relaxation tend to see all stress as bad.

There are good things to be said about stress. In fact, some stress is necessary to human functioning. Without stress who would write a poem, solve a problem, or start a business? You might say stress is one of the things that separate the humans from the vegetables— unless you are the scientist who wrote a treatise on the effect of stress on plants. As you practice the relaxation technique(s) of your choice it may be worthwhile to remember that all stress is not to be eliminated. Keep some to motivate you to achieve something.

Relaxation's popularity continues to grow as more people become aware of its effectiveness. Individuals can consider a variety of relaxation techniques and choose one that fits their needs. Some techniques take longer than others, but there has been considerable documentation of their effectiveness. With the increased realization of the damaging effects of too much stress, the increased skepticism of the idea of taking a pill to cure every malady, and the increased cost of health care, the use of self-help relaxation techniques can only increase.

In addition to the new relaxation techniques that will develop in the future, I suspect there will be further development of the technique of visualization. The power of the human mind is infinite. Visualization is the technique that will benefit most from the tremendous capabilities of television, particularly when combined with the computer. The biofeedback potential of the computer has hardly been tapped.

Progressive relaxation is so easy and useful to so many people that it will continue to be the relaxation technique of choice for most individuals. The recent introduction of small portable cassette tape players (like the popular WALKMAN) makes it possible to relax to a tape in almost any environment. This increases the usefulness of a taped narration.

The recent explosion in technology also promises to continue to change the methods of instruction in relaxation techniques. Although the recent increase in videotapes presents a magnificent opportunity to expand education in all areas, it seems to me that it is limited when it comes to helping people to learn more about such techniques as progressive relaxation, meditation, and autogenics. The reason for this is that these are not visual methods.

Hypnosis has been in and out of favor in its 5000-year history. Currently it seems to be gaining acceptance again. Although it is used for many other purposes as well, hypnosis still provides an effective relaxation technique. The primary drawback, especially for those with limited funds, is that a person must go to a trained hypnotist to have the

Theories of Relaxation

---

technique applied. A relaxation narration can be considered an informal hypnosis, but all it requires is a cassette tape or a friend with a soothing reading voice.

In the years in which I have used and taught these procedures I have become convinced that what is called hypnosis is nothing more than deep relaxation. I agree with the expert who has said, "the only difference between relaxation procedures and hypnotic induction procedures is the name given them". (Coleman, 1976, as quoted in Edmonston, 1981).

FEEL BETTER! LIVE LONGER! RELAX

3.Techniques of Relaxation

There are two approaches to relaxation. One is using the muscles to relax and the other is using the mind. Later on, you will be able to combine the two, but in starting out it is better to learn them separately. Regardless of the technique used to relax, body position is very important. The goal is to give every muscle possible a rest. The less muscle tension that exists in the body during relaxation, the deeper the relaxation.

The best chair to use is a recliner. You have support for your head, armrests for your arms, and leg rests that, ideally, support your feet as well as your legs. Most reclining chairs are adjustable enough that you can get into a very comfortable position. If you can only use a straight or arm chair you will probably need to spend a little more time and effort adjusting your position. If your head can rest against something (the chair itself or a wall) without tensing any muscles, that's fine. If not, perhaps you can add a pillow or rolled-up blanket. If you can't find a way of supporting your head simply leave it straight up. A helpful thought is to imagine it balancing on your spine. DO NOT LET YOUR HEAD FALL EITHER FORWARD OR BACK. Doing this will only cause you to be distracted during the relaxation itself and will probably give you a sore neck at the end. If possible, rest your arms on armrests, but if there are none allow your hands to rest on your lap. Let your feet sit flat on the floor but adjust them forward or back until the muscle tension in the front of your ankle is about equal to that behind your ankle. DO NOT CROSS YOUR LEGS OR, IF POSSIBLE, TOUCH YOURSELF ANYWHERE. The reason for this is that you may cause a blockage in circulation in this manner or, at least, run the risk of distracting yourself.

If a prone position seems more practical to you, that is certainly acceptable. The only problem with lying down is that a person is likely to go to sleep and while there's nothing wrong with that in itself, it does slow down the process of learning the relaxation technique being used. Remember, the purpose at first is to learn these techniques, not simply do them. If you decide to lie down while practicing one of the techniques, lie on your back on a comfortable but firm surface such as a hard mattress or a mat on the floor. Place a small pillow or rolled-up blanket under your head and another under your knees. Let your hands lie at your side without touching your body and keep your face straight up.

In addition to a comfortable position another require-ment for relaxation is a quiet, dark room. If you are alone in your home or office and there is a telephone, unplug it so that you will not be disturbed. Take any other steps you feel are indicated to insure that you are not bothered during your relaxation.

Techniques of Relaxation

Another important prerequisite to relaxation is a passive, but positive, attitude. One must not be in the middle of wrestling with some horrendous mental problem. Later, though, after you get proficient at relaxation you should be able to relax in order to solve a problem. When I say assume a positive attitude, I mean that you must believe that the relaxation will work.

As I have indicated before, you may be somewhat anxious as you begin your first relaxation technique, but this is perfectly normal and will go away as you relax.

a. Passive Progressive Relaxation

Both passive and active progressive relaxation stem from the work of Dr. Edmund Jacobson, physician and physiologist. Dr. Jacobson began his research in 1908 at Harvard University, later moving to Chicago where the bulk of his work was done. He devised a method by which a doctor-teacher would train individuals to relax each limb or group of muscles individually. The entire period of training took weeks, months, or even years. Dr. Jacobson, in his later books, began to consider the possibility that individuals could train themselves in progressive relaxation techniques. He would be surprised to see how far the field he virtually began has now come.

The following passive progressive relaxation narration (which I have titled LIVE LONGER, RELAX) is the easiest of

FEEL BETTER! LIVE LONGER! RELAX

the various techniques to practice. It requires no effort on your part other than simply relaxing as the voice on the tape tells you to relax specific muscles or muscle groups. My reason for including this script is that this will enable the reader to record his own relaxation narration or have someone read it to him/her. It probably will not be practical to read the script to yourself (reading takes too much mental effort to be compatible with relaxation) but it may well be possible to memorize it.

Here is the script of LIVE LONGER, RELAX:

LIVE LONGER, RELAX

Feel free to adjust the volume of this tape to a level that seems peaceful and comfortable to you. Find yourself a comfortable chair and we will begin. If possible see that your head is well supported and that your arms are resting on arm rests. Let your feet sit flat on the floor. Slowly let your mind drift through your body and check out your body positions. Make sure you are just as comfortable as you can be. Watch

Techniques of Relaxation

that your clothing doesn't restrict you anywhere. Now allow your eyes to close and let your thoughts drift to the top of your head, to your scalp. Smooth out the muscles in your scalp. Relax your scalp muscles and let your scalp rest easily on the top of your head. (pause)

Now relax your forehead muscles and let that relaxation flow down over your eye lids. Allow the flow to continue down over your cheeks, lips, and chin, letting your whole face become relaxed. Let your jaw muscles relax, allow your jaw to drop a little if it wants to. Permit your tongue to rest comfortably on the floor of your mouth. All the muscles of your head are relaxed now. They feel comfortably heavy . . . comfortably heavy. (pause)

Now allow the relaxation to flow down your neck and into your shoulders. Smooth out the muscles of your neck and shoulders. Let them be limp and relaxed. Imagine the muscles as knotted ropes that you untie and let hang loose. (pause)

Continue the relaxation in your shoulders, neck, and head while you allow the relaxation to flow down into your upper arms. Relax the muscles of your upper arms, smoothing them out and letting them go. (pause)

Now let that relaxation flow into your forearms. Relax the muscles of your forearms. Your arms are feeling comfortably heavy and warm. (pause)

Let your hands and fingers relax. Feel the blood flowing comfortably in to your fingertips. Your hands and arms are heavy and warm . . . heavy and warm. (pause)

Techniques of Relaxation

Keep your head and neck, shoulders and arms, relaxed while you let your mind drift to your upper back. Smooth out all the muscles in your upper back and relax them. Allow the muscles to relax down your spine, just letting go. (pause)

Let that relaxation come around your body, smoothing out the muscles around your rib cage. As you breathe, allow your chest to become more and more comfortably relaxed. Feel every breath. Inhale through your nostrils. Take one deep breath, filling up your lungs and then exhaling back out again. (pause)

Now resume your normal breathing and let it be rhythmic and smooth . . . rhythmic and smooth. As you take each breath let yourself float down into the chair. (pause)

FEEL BETTER! LIVE LONGER! RELAX

Now allow the relaxation to spread down into your abdomen and hips, smoothing out all the muscles. (pause)

Let that feeling flow down into your thighs and relax the muscles in your upper legs. Smooth them out and let them go . (pause)

Now let the relaxation flow into the calves of your legs. Smooth out the muscles of your lower legs, causing your legs to be comfortably relaxed. They are heavy and warm. (pause)

The relaxation flows down into your feet, relaxing the soles of your feet and your toes. Think of your toes getting warm as the blood flows easily to them. (pause)

Techniques of Relaxation

Now your whole body, from the top of your head to the tips of your toes is relaxed and peaceful. You're comfortable both inside and out. With every breath allow your body to let go a little more. Float on down into the chair, comfortably heavy and relaxed. Be assured that everything is going to be all right. (pause)

As you're comfortably relaxing remain awake and aware, but very relaxed. Relaxation allows your whole body to have a very deep rest while you're completely aware and awake. (pause)

Through deep muscle relaxation such as you are experiencing now your body will feel refreshed. As you listen to this tape over and over and eventually memorize it you will find

43

yourself more and more capable of deep relaxation. You will relax more quickly and more efficiently. Soon you will become so skilled at relaxing that simply by saying the words "calm", "heavy and warm", or whatever words you choose, you will be able to achieve the same degree of deep relaxation you are experiencing now. With practice the relaxation will become even deeper. (pause)

Feel free to continue to relax as long as you wish, or if you are ready, allow yourself to become aware of your surroundings and allow your eyes to open while remaining relaxed, feeling good, and refreshed.—

Those of you who have heard progressive relaxation narrations previously may have heard them in the reverse order from this one, i.e. from toe to head rather than from head to toe. Many narrators follow this upward procedure,

Techniques of Relaxation

but I feel that the sensation of going down as well as the opportunity to use the word 'down' makes the head-to-toe direction of the narration preferable. However, if you like the toe-to-head direction by all means use it. Whatever works for you is the method you should use.

b. Active Progressive Relaxation

Active Progressive Relaxation is also known as the Tension-Relaxation technique. Jacobson believed that it is extremely important for the relaxing individual to be able to distinguish between tension and relaxation (remember we are still discussing a muscle technique).

This tends to be difficult for persons who suffer from arthritis or similar painful conditions. When they tense certain muscles they feel pain, and pain is certainly not any help to relaxation. (Although relaxation for the control of pain is one of the benefits that can be achieved at a more advanced level.) I have had arthritic clients who were able to use this technique by simply skipping the instruction that they knew was going to hurt them.

This technique is particularly beneficial for those who suffer from muscle spasms although it should be tried by everyone who is evaluating relaxation techniques. There is almost no way of knowing which of the various techniques will appeal to any one individual.

FEEL BETTER! LIVE LONGER! RELAX

The verbatim script follows:

ACTIVE RELAXATION

Adjust the volume of the tape recorder so that it is comfortable for you. If possible see that your head is well supported and that your arms are resting on arm rests. Let your feet sit flat on the floor. Slowly, let your mind drift through your body and check out your body positions. Your clothes shouldn't restrict you anywhere. Now allow your eyes to close and just relax all over. You are comfortable. The tension has gone out of every muscle in your body. As you're relaxing and comfortable, clench your right fist. Hard! As you clench your fist tighter and tighter, examine the tension in your right fist and forearm. Now - relax. As the fingers of your right hand loosen think about the contrast you have

Techniques of Relaxation

---

just experienced between tension and relaxation. (pause)

Let the relaxation spread and allow yourself to become more relaxed all over. (pause)

Again, clench your right fist. Clench it! Hold it tightly! Noticing the tension. Tighter! Tighter! Now—relax. Again notice the contrast. (pause)

Clench your left fist. Clench that fist tighter! Continue to clench your left fist while you let the rest of your body relax. Now relax totally. Enjoy the contrast between the tension and relaxation. (pause)

Now clench your left fist again. Hold it tight! Relax. Feel the contrast. Let yourself relax all over for awhile. (pause)

FEEL BETTER! LIVE LONGER! RELAX

Now, clench both fists. This time make sure your forearms are tense as well as your hands. Tighter! Tighter! Relax. Let your fingers straighten out naturally. Relax more and more. Hands and forearms and all over. Continue to relax for awhile. (pause)

Now tense the muscles of your upper arms. Hold the tension in your upper arms. Think about that tension. Now relax. Notice how it feels, both when you tense up and when you relax. Tighten your upper arm muscles again. Feel that tension. Now relax. Observe your feelings once more as you go from tension to relaxation. (pause)

Now hold your arms out straight in front of you and tighten the muscles along the back of your upper arms. Stretch and tense! Now relax. Lower your arms back to

Techniques of Relaxation

---

where they were. Your arms feel comfortably heavy as they relax. Now let's think about pure relaxation flowing into your arms. Let your arms relax more and more. When you think your arms are fully relaxed, go a little bit further. (pause)

Now let all your muscles relax. Feeling loose and heavy. Let's just relax all over for awhile. (pause)

Now think about your forehead. Raise your eyebrows as high as you can. Wrinkle up your forehead. Wrinkle it tighter. Now relax. Smooth out your forehead. Think about your forehead and scalp becoming smoother as the relaxation flows over them. (pause)

Now lower your eyebrows as much as you can causing your forehead to frown. Study the tension. Now relax and smooth out your forehead again. (pause)

Now squeeze your eyes shut. Close them tighter. Hold that tension! Now relax your eyes. Keep them closed while you notice the relaxation. (pause)

Clench your jaws. Think about the tension in them. Now relax your jaws. Let your lips part slightly if they want to. Now press your tongue up against the roof of your mouth. Notice the tension .Now relax your tongue and press your lips together. Tighter! Now relax your lips and observe the change as they go from tension to relaxation. Feel the relaxation all over your face and forehead, thinking particularly about your scalp, eyes, jaws, tongue, and your lips. (pause)

Techniques of Relaxation

Now lean your head back as far as you can and feel the tension in the front of your neck. Roll your head to the right and feel the tension in the left side of your neck. Continue rolling your head forward until your chin is against your chest. Feel the strain in the back of your neck. Roll your head on to the left and notice the tension in the right side of your neck. Now let your head roll completely around twice, before you return to a comfortable, straight-up position and relax. (pause)

Now raise your shoulders. Try to touch your ears with them. Hold them up there! Relax. Drop your shoulders. Both your neck and your shoulders are relaxed now. (pause)

Shrug your shoulders up again and then move them forward and back several times. Notice the tension in your shoulders and upper back. Now relax and let that relaxation flow deeply into your shoulders and back muscles. Relax all your muscles now as the pure relaxation becomes deeper . . . deeper . . . deeper. (pause)

Continue relaxing all over. You feel as though you're floating and, at the same time, you're comfortably heavy. Breathe easily and normally. Observe the relaxation deepen each time you exhale. Feel the relaxation as you breathe out. Now try breathing in deeply and holding your breath. Observe the tension. Let your mind think about the muscles of your chest and how tight they are. Now exhale. Just relax and breathe freely. Each time you exhale feel the walls of your chest grow loose. Continue relaxing. (pause)

As your body continues to relax, breathe in deeply now and hold it again. Breathe out and notice the relaxation.

Techniques of Relaxation

Continue to breathe easily and normally. Let the relaxation you feel in your chest spread to your back. Now let go even more and enjoy the relaxation. (pause)

Now let's go to your abdominal muscles. Imagine that you're preparing to receive a blow in the stomach. Tighten your stomach muscles so that your abdomen is hard. Notice the tension - and then relax. Think about the contrast. Once again, tighten your stomach muscles, making your abdomen hard. Hold it like that. Study the tension - and then relax. See how you feel good all over. (pause)

Now pull your stomach muscles in. Try to make your abdomen press against your backbone. Hold it there. Feel the tension! And now relax. Breathe normally for awhile and feel the massaging action on your abdomen and chest. Now pull your stomach in again and feel the tension. Relax. Let that relaxation go deeper and deeper. Breathing normally, feel that relaxation increase each time you exhale. Continue relaxing. Let yourself enjoy the relaxation. (pause)

Now let your mind travel to your lower back. Arch your back so that there is a hollow between your lower back and the chair you're sitting in. Feel the tension in your lower back—and then relax. Again, arch your back and feel the tension. Localize the tension, trying to relax the rest of your body while continuing to tense your lower back. Completely relax. Let the relaxation spread throughout your body. (pause)

Now tighten the muscles in your buttocks and thighs. Press your heels down into the floor as hard as you can.

Techniques of Relaxation

Relax. Now tense those same muscles again. Hold the tension! Now relax. Relax your hips, thighs, and legs. Let the relaxation spread throughout your body. Let all the tension go. (pause)

Let the relaxation go deeper and deeper. Relax your feet, the muscles of your lower legs, your thighs and hips. The whole lower part of your body feels heavy. (pause)

Let the relaxation spread upward to your stomach and lower back, then to your chest and upper back. Now relax your shoulders, arms, and neck. As the relaxation proceeds it is also getting deeper and deeper. (pause)

Now relax your facial and head muscles. You are now deeply relaxed all over your body. Your whole body feels heavy now and you're very comfortable in your chair. (pause)

Take a long, deep breath and let it out slowly. Keep relaxing for awhile. (pause)

When you're ready, allow yourself to become aware of your surroundings. You will be alert, refreshed, and relaxed...

c. Visualization

We now switch from muscle techniques of relaxation to mind techniques of relaxation. Visualization (or imagery) is, for many, the best relaxation technique. It involves seeing in your mind a favorite, very pleasant place. It is possible to choose a place that you imagine, but most people go in their minds to a remembered place. Although visualization begins by seeing a scene, it develops (over time and with practice) into feeling yourself as part of the scene. The scene selected should involve as many senses as possible. An example might be an ocean beach visualization in which you feel the warmth of the sun and the rough sand of the beach (touch),

Techniques of Relaxation

you hear the sound of the waves and the gulls (sound), you see the brightness of the sun and the blue of the ocean (sight), you smell the scents of the ocean (smell), and you taste the salt in the air (taste). Another idea is a forest scene in which you see and smell the flowers, and hear and feel the wind.

Another important point concerning visualization is that you should be alone in the scene. If there is a fisherman across a lake or a dog next to you, that is certainly all right, but having a loved one by your side is not recommended. The reason for this is that we all have mixed feelings about the important people in our life and strong emotion is not conducive to relaxation. As in other techniques of relaxation, it is important to have a feeling of warmth accompanying the scene. The most important single factor, though, is that it be an extremely pleasant scene for you.

This technique is not for everyone. Theodore X. Barber, a psychologist who has done some of the most important work on hypnotism, points out that fantasy prone persons who are very good at visualizing and have a rich imagination make excellent hypnotic subjects. Barber estimates that only 5% of the population is in this category.

Some of the people I have worked with have visualized beach scenes (many times these are specific beaches such as Maui or in the Caribbean). Others visualized being in the forest or near a tranquil mountain lake, sitting in front of a roaring fire in a cozy mountain cabin, or running through a cornfield next to a beloved pet (this was a childhood memory). Other imagery included sitting on a rock in the middle of a stream (I thought this wasn't warm enough, but that didn't seem to bother the woman who visualized the scene), and viewing the mountains in the distance from a highway rest stop in the California desert. This latter visualization was by a woman who was a psychotherapy client of mine and she told me one day that a black cloud had come over her scene the day before. Inquiry revealed that her best friend had gone into the hospital that day with cancer.

The ability to visualize increases with repeated visualizations. It is wise to stay with the same visualization, at least after trying several to see which is most relaxing. If visualization does not come easy to you, here are several methods of improving your skills.

One is to practice visualizing scenes of differing complexity. According to Samuels, everyone can visualize the bedroom they slept in during childhood or adolescence. The details will become clearer and clearer as we repeatedly return to this room. Unfortunately, for some people, it may not be a relaxing or happy visualization but it will probably be easy to attain. As you get better and better at visualizing your room you can move on to other familiar scenes that may be more pleasant. Remember, although it is called visualization, this technique will develop to the point where you will feel yourself in your chosen scene. Also, as you get better and better at it, the position you assume will become

---

less and less important.

The second aid to visualizing is to listen to a narration of a scene and participate in its sensations. One of the DIMI-TAPES is called RELAX ON THE BEACH. Here is a script for that narration:

RELAX ON THE BEACH
You are now going to relax on the beach. Although this

experience takes place in your mind it will be quite real to

you. Get into a comfortable position either in a chair or lying

down. Make sure that the volume on the tape recorder is

adjusted to a comfortable level. As you settle down let your

eyes close and allow yourself to relax. Just let go of all your

tensions. Now breathe in deeply and let the air out slowly.

Inhale again and exhale slowly again. Breathe normally

now and allow yourself to feel your body lying on the warm

beach. The soft sand shapes itself to the contours of your

body. (pause)

You are more and more relaxed as you feel yourself lying comfortably on the sand. (pause)

You feel the warm rays of the sun on your face and body. (pause)

You hear the sounds of the ocean waves breaking on the shore. (pause)

From time to time you hear the cries of the gulls wheeling over head. (pause)

You smell the salt spray in the air. (pause)

You feel good. (pause)

Techniques of Relaxation

You are happy. (pause)

Your breathing is rhythmic and smooth . . . rhythmic and smooth. (pause)

You are at peace with yourself. (pause)

You are warm and comfortable. (pause)

You are calm and relaxed. (pause)

You are happy. (pause)

You're letting go of the tension in your body more and

more as you relax on the beach. (pause)

The gentle golden sunlight is peaceful and healing. (pause)

You are healthy. (pause)

It's good to feel the sand under your body and the warm rays of the sun above. (pause)

It's good to hear the sound of the waves and the gulls. (pause)

It's good to smell the salt spray. (pause)

Techniques of Relaxation

You are happy and self-confident. (pause)

Now let's continue to rest on the beach, feeling the warmth of the sun, hearing the waves and the gulls, and smelling the salt spray. I'm going to stop talking for a couple of minutes now while you continue to relax.

(Pause for two minutes)

The gentle golden sunlight is peaceful and healing. (pause)

You are healthy, happy, calm, and very relaxed. (pause)

The feelings of calmness, of health, and of happiness will be with you throughout the day and throughout the coming week.

Let's just rest on the warm, soft sand for another minute.

(Pause for one minute)

Anytime that you like in the coming week, you can return to this calm, beautiful scene once again. (pause)

You can do this by closing your eyes, breathing in deeply and exhaling slowly, and seeing in your mind this warm, peaceful beach. (pause)

You can feel yourself lying on the comfortable sand. (pause)

You can hear the sounds of the ocean. (pause)

Techniques of Relaxation

You can smell the smells of the ocean. (Pause)

You will be able to return to this scene whenever you like.

Now, as our time on the beach draws to a close, I'm going to count gradually from one to five.

You will awake at the count of five.

You will bring with you into your alert state the feelings you have had of calmness, happiness, and health.

At one, you feel yourself leaving the beach and returning to the room.

At two, you feel your calm heartbeat as you become more and more alert.

Three, you are even more alert.

Four, you begin to open your eyes and—

Five, you are completely awake.

Take a deep breath and stretch— —

d. Meditation

Like most of the other relaxation techniques, meditation is used for other purposes besides relaxation. As LeShan

Techniques of Relaxation

writes, the two major psychological effects (or common results) of consistent meditation are, "the attainment of another way of perceiving and relating to reality and a greater efficiency and enthusiasm in everyday life". My purpose here is to teach meditation as a means to relax and thus I will not spend a great deal of time on the more exotic (and difficult) types of meditation. As I pointed out in the history of relaxation section, meditation has developed in many cultures as a means of an individual 'getting in touch with reality', or 'achieving union with the All (or with God)'.

Although we usually associate meditation with India, it has also appeared in the fifth to twelfth centuries in the Syrian and Jordanian deserts, in tenth-century Japan, in medieval European monasteries, in Poland and Russia in the eighteenth and nineteenth centuries and at other times and places.

Some of the more familiar schools of meditation are the Zen, Yoga, and Sufi. These and most others are based on the contemplation of a specific object for the purpose of allowing the mind to focus on reality (or God). There are numerous other methods of meditation. Some involve counting each breath in focusing on imaginary objects (such as bubbles), others involve focusing one's mind on repeated words or phrases. The latter method, sometimes called chanting a 'mantra' is used by both TRANSCENDENTAL MEDITATION and for invoking the RELAXATION RESPONSE using Benson's technique. Meditation is considered very difficult to master and the use of a teacher is almost mandatory.

TRANSCENDENTAL MEDITATION was the first form of meditation widely used in the United States. It is specifically not a religion or a philosophy. It is solely a method of meditation and was introduced into the U.S. by its chief proponent, Maharishi Mahesh Yogi, in 1959. It became a big business, having at one time 380 centers in the U.S. alone. The followers of TM established a university, announced a World Plan, and proposed such modest goals as lowering the world's crime rate. In the words of one of the most enthusiastic books promoting the method, TM, DISCOVERING INNER ENERGY AND OVERCOMING STRESS, "We are standing before the dawn of what is to be one of the greatest transformations in human history." Maharishi Mahesh Yogi claimed, at one time, to have over half a million practitioners of TM in the U.S., not counting those elsewhere in the world.

It has, without a doubt, resulted in the practice of meditation by far more people in the Western world than have ever done this before. I'm not sure that TRANSCENDENTAL MEDITATION has lowered the world's crime rate, but it certainly has done a lot of good for a lot of people.

Unfortunately, TM has had some negative aspects. The organization behind it obviously became a money-making scheme and a huge enterprise. TM can only be taught by approved 'teachers' who charge a sizeable fee. This structure is not entirely bad as meditation IS best learned from a

Techniques of Relaxation

teacher. Also, it is certainly motivating to use something if you've paid money for it.

One of the important features of TM is to provide each student with a 'mantra', which is a secret word given to the student by his/her teacher and, supposedly, designed specifically for him/her. As indicated earlier a 'mantra' is an integral part of many systems of meditation. It was discovered and reported in the magazine PSYCHOLOGY TODAY that TM's mantra is one of twelve words that are distributed to each student on the basis of his/her month of birth. So much for the "personally selected" mantra. The phrase "personally selected" comes from another self-promoting book on TM called THE TM BOOK. As I've indicated, despite the negatives of the TM movement, the introduction into this society of an easily attainable and widely acceptable method of meditation is all for the good. It has undoubtedly helped many, many people relax.

Perhaps its greatest benefit to readers of this book is that it led a Western scientist to objectively measure the benefits of TM, be impressed by it, and proceed to develop a simple, inexpensive westernized method of achieving a meditative state. This scientist was Dr. Herbert Benson, a Harvard cardiologist, and the method he developed elicits what he calls the RELAXATION RESPONSE. Let Benson himself relate how this began:

"In 1968, practitioners of Transcendental Meditation

FEEL BETTER! LIVE LONGER! RELAX

came to   the laboratory at the Harvard Medical School, where we were in the midst of studying the relation between a monkey's behavior and his blood pressure. These devotees of meditation asked whether they could be studied, for they felt they could lower their blood pressure through Transcendental Meditation. They were turned away with a polite 'Thank you'. Why investigate anything so far out as meditation?"

The TM people persisted, and Benson finally relented and began investigations to determine whether meditation could lower blood pressure. His research was conducted independently of other medical research being done at the time. He began by reviewing studies that had been done on meditation and found a bewildering array of cases and results. The varied meditative techniques, combined with the uneven expertise of the meditators, made any truly scientific evaluation of meditation virtually impossible. However, TM provided a simple technique carried out under reasonably uniform conditions.

Early on in his investigations, Benson found that TM practitioners consistently and significantly lowered their oxygen consumption, blood lactate level, brain-wave activity, heart rate, and rate of breathing while meditating. What did not change was blood pressure. The TM people had already lowered their blood pressure by their repeated use of meditation. In this phase of his research, Benson used young, healthy subjects, most of whom had been practicing

Techniques of Relaxation

Transcendental Meditation for two or three years.

He then began experiments on people just learning TM. He isolated over 80 people who had high blood pressure before they signed up to learn TM, then reduced that number to 36 who had not changed their medication or were not taking any. He wanted to be sure that the results of the study reflected the effects of meditation only, and not altered medication. To digress a moment, I would like to note that the rigorousness of Dr. Benson's research techniques was admirable. For example, he used a special machine in taking blood pressures which muddles the numbers and deciphers them only after the measurement has been made. The purpose of this was to eliminate possible observer bias. He also took his subjects' blood pressure for six weeks before they began the TM program.

The results of this experiment were that after several weeks of practicing TM the subjects' average blood pressure dropped from 146/93.5 to 137/88.9. This constitutes a drop from the borderline high blood pressure range into the normal range. It is statistically significant. All blood pressure measurements were taken during periods of the day unrelated to meditation and thus indicate a basic change in blood pressure.

Further research indicated, though, that this beneficial drop in blood pressure was maintained only if the subjects continued to practice TM. When seven of the subjects chose to stop meditating their blood pressure returned to their initial hypertensive levels within four weeks. Thus we see that while meditation lowers blood pressure it does not cure high blood pressure. The meditation, or probably any other relaxation technique, must be continued to continue the lowered blood pressure.

After the investigations, and after studying the literature on meditation, Benson proceeded to develop an extremely easy set of instructions for bringing forth the RELAXATION RESPONSE. Benson was careful to point out that his method was not superior to TM or any other meditative technique but was easier and cheaper. For the purpose of relaxation it was just as good. It might not be as effective in meeting some of the other goals of meditation, such as union with God. Prayer, which has elements of meditation, is also an effective method of reaching the RELAXATION RESPONSE, even though that is not its primary goal.

Benson's method is, as I've indicated, a simplified adaptation of TRANSCENDENTAL MEDITATION which is, in turn, a simple method of meditation.

It consists of four essential elements:

1. A Quiet Environment

2. A Mental Device - Benson recommends simply repeat-

Techniques of Relaxation

ing a neutral word, such as ONE, with each exhalation of breath.

3. A Passive Attitude - Benson considers this the most important of the four elements.

4. A Comfortable Position

In order to convey in more depth the method Benson has developed, I am including at this point a script of my narration called HOW TO MEDITATE. It is DIMI-TAPE #16 and includes #1 on the reverse side. The reason for this combination is that a Passive Progressive Relaxation is an excellent way to begin a period of meditation. Here is HOW TO MEDITATE:

DIMI-TAPE #16 - HOW TO MEDITATE

You can learn to meditate. I'm going to instruct you in a simple, easy-to-learn method and then help you get started. Unfortunately, the practice of meditation has too often been taught under the auspices of Eastern religions, and surrounded by cultures and peoples with which most of us are unfamiliar.

This is not necessary, as the benefits of meditation can be gained by anyone. There is no need to be mystical or mysterious about it.

There are four essential elements to meditation.

First, a quiet place. The quieter, the better. If you like to have some quiet music playing in the background, that's okay, but otherwise there should be as little noise as possible.

Second, a comfortable position. Sitting in a reclining chair or lying down is good, but meditation can be practiced in an ordinary armchair or even a straight chair. The most important considerations in being in a comfortable position are to support your limbs and head, if at all possible, and balance what cannot be supported. Unless you're using a reclining chair or are lying down put your feet flat on the floor, extend your legs at a comfortable angle, balance your head on your spine. Make sure that all your muscles are equally relaxed. If you like, you may find it practical to sit at your desk while you meditate. Also, I'd suggest that you loosen tight clothing, take off your glasses and your shoes, if you want to.

The third of the four essential elements for meditation may be the most important. It is simply a passive attitude. Attempt to empty your mind of all thoughts. As thoughts, and other perceptions drift into your consciousness just be passive and let them drift on. Don't worry about how well you're doing. Just let the mental stimuli flow over you and

Techniques of Relaxation

away, like water in a moving stream. It may be hard for you to assume this passive attitude at first but keep at it. It'll work for you.

The fourth essential element is what people frequently think meditation is all about. It's really just one of the four fundamental components. It is something to focus your mind upon. You notice I use the word focus, rather than concentrate, because concentrate sounds like work. Meditation should never be work, but simply something you allow to happen. Whatever it is you choose to focus upon, it should be constant. In other words, do not focus on something that will go away. Many people gaze fixedly at something. Objects that have been used include a candle flame, a color wheel, or a spot on a plain background.

A sound may be used rather than a material object. A meaningless sound, a word, or even a phrase may be repeated, either silently or aloud. If you use a sound you can keep your eyes closed, which is good. An excellent method is to visualize an object. See it in your mind's eye, so to speak. If you can focus on an object seen only in your mind, you can also keep your eyes closed. While you focus upon whatever you choose, pay attention to the rhythm of your breathing. If possible, breathe through your nose.

Let me now suggest a specific way to meditate. Find a quiet place, get in a comfortable position, assume a passive attitude, and become aware of your regular breathing.

Now, as you breathe out, say the word 'one' silently to yourself. Let me demonstrate: breathe in . . . out. In . . . 'one'. In . . . 'one'. Continue this for ten minutes or so. If you want to open your eyes to check the time, feel free, but don't set an alarm. When you finish meditating rest quietly for a few minutes, first with your eyes closed and then with them open. Then stand up slowly and resume your normal activities.

It isn't necessary to meditate for exactly ten minutes at a time. Less than five minutes at a time will be ineffective and more than 20 unnecessary. You should meditate twice a day. If you use meditation to put yourself to sleep after going to bed, you should meditate twice a day in addition. It's fine to put yourself to sleep with meditation but the best effects on your body and its tension come when you're meditating without going to sleep.

A frequent problem that beginning meditators have is the occurrence of distracting thoughts. Don't struggle with these intruding thoughts. Simply try to ignore them and continue focusing on the sound or object you have chosen. With practice it will become easy to ignore the distracting thoughts.

By the way, meditation is less effective within two hours after a meal. It won't do any harm, but you can't relax as much when the body's digestive processes are going on.

Techniques of Relaxation

I want to emphasize that the choice of an object to meditate upon is strictly up to you. I have suggested the silently repeated word 'one' but there's no reason why you have to use that. Whatever you choose as your object it should be emotionally neutral. Once you've decided upon an object to focus upon don't change to another. Be consistent. If you can, establish regular times in your day to meditate.

Meditation has helped many people in many ways and there's no reason it can't help you. People have been able to lower their blood pressure, reduce their headaches, relieve their muscle tension, and relax their mental anxieties. Many have become more effective at what they do, happier and more pleasant for others to be around. You can almost certainly fit meditation into your schedule if you try. One idea is to replace coffee breaks with meditation breaks. But other creative ways of freeing up time may be arranged. In order to help you get started with meditating I've recorded a relaxation narration on the reverse side of this tape. This relaxation narration is of the type called 'progressive relaxation' and focuses on relaxing your muscles. You will find it very helpful in attaining the passive attitude so important to meditation. Listen to it before you begin to meditate. Soon you will be able to relax your muscles without listening to the tape and then you'll move into the meditation itself sooner.

Be sure to let yourself float into the meditation easily after the relaxation itself.

I'll review the four essential components to meditation:

One, a quiet place.

Two, a comfortable position.

Three, a passive attitude, and,

Four, something to focus your mind upon.

Remember, as you begin meditating focus your mind upon something you have selected. I recommend that it be the nonemotional word 'one' and that you say the word to yourself each time that you exhale. Breathe in a normal rhythm.

Now, whenever you're ready, find a quiet place, assume a comfortable position, listen to the other side of this tape as the first step in achieving a passive attitude and then move into meditating itself. If you have any difficulties, feel free to write me. My name is Dick Lutz and my address is 3820 Oak Hollow Lane, SE, Salem, Oregon 97302.

Good meditating!

Techniques of Relaxation

e. Hypnosis

Hypnosis is perhaps the oldest of the techniques of relaxation described in this book. Hypnosis can be considered nothing more than relaxation induced by someone else, while self-hypnosis is, obviously, self-induced.

Relaxation tapes are actually hypnotic because they induce an 'altered state of consciousness', which, most authorities agree, is what hypnosis is. Edmonston, in his book HYPNOSIS AND RELAXATION, says simply "Traditional hypnosis, . . , is basically and fundamentally relaxation". I tend to agree with Edmonston (although I don't disagree with the other authorities) and feel that hypnosis and relaxation are the same thing.

When hypnosis is used in the treatment of emotional disorders it is called hypnotherapy. It can be used for many purposes. As Dr. Milton V. Kline says in his foreword to Dr. William Kroger's classic CLINICAL AND EXPERIMENTAL HYPNOSIS, "Clinical hypnosis as an integral technique in psychotherapy has made significant contributions to the management of a wide range of psychological and medical problems". Many of the specific problems are listed in Chapter 4 of this book and will not be discussed here. Some of the more general problems dealt with by hypnotherapists include psychosomatic illness, the management of pain, and both neurotic and psychotic disturbances. Hypnosis has been used in the treatment of post-traumatic syndromes and specific physical disorders such as cerebral palsy and multiple sclerosis.

I cannot think of any psychological or physical disorder in which hypnotism is inappropriate or obviously useless. Hypnotism is used quite effectively in dentistry and in childbirth. When hypnosis is used as an adjunct to psychoanalysis, the process is called hypnoanalysis and speeds up the lengthy (and expensive) process of psychoanalysis. A listing of the uses of hypnotism could go on and on, but in this book the focus is on relaxation. Hypnosis is a very effective technique for attaining relaxation, whether you choose to use self-hypnosis (sometimes called auto-hypnosis) or hypnosis induced by a hypnotist.

An unfortunate (and misleading) practice of hypnotism is its use in entertainment. This is frequently called 'stage hypnotism'. Stage hypnotism is illegal in my state (Oregon) as well as in several other states and in many countries of the world. Where used, stage hypnotism usually involves an entertainer hypnotizing (or sometimes only pretending to) an individual or individuals for the purpose of amusing an audience. The hypnotist usually suggests that the subject(s) perform some outlandish stunt such as barking like a dog or clucking like a chicken. This is amusing to the audience but anxiety-producing for anybody who may later think of using hypnotism for some serious purpose.

Techniques of Relaxation

Hypnotism cannot be used to force a person to do something against his/her principles. The stage hypnotist may ask a person to do something silly, but he can't get away with causing a person to commit a crime (unless that person is already a criminal). A hypnotized person does not lose consciousness. He/she is not under the control of the hypnotist. He may follow the hypnotist's suggestion but only if he wants to (or is willing to).

Almost everyone can be hypnotized, at least to some extent, and it is a most relaxing, rewarding experience for most.

Hypnosis has been practised for at least 5000 years and may have been used before that. According to Kroger in his work CLINICAL AND EXPERIMENTAL HYPNOSIS, "hypnosis produces a greater state of relaxation than do any of the other methods for inducing relaxation". In my experience, this statement is usually true but there are certain individuals for whom hypnosis is not effective. These tend to be people who, for one reason or another, are unduly anxious about hypnosis as a procedure. Mild anxiety about any new experience is normal and can be overcome but extreme anxiety is counter-productive.

There are a few religious groups which are opposed to hypnosis and this certainly causes a problem in the use of hypnosis by their adherents. These denominations include Christian Scientists, Seventh Day Adventists, Jehovah's

Witnesses, and certain fundamentalist Christians. On the other hand, all mainstream Protestant denominations either support the appropriate use of hypnosis or take no stand on the matter. The Roman Catholic Church has gone even further in support of the use of hypnosis. In 1847 and again in 1956, the Pope endorsed the use of hypnosis. As far as I am aware, no non-Christian religions oppose hypnosis and many incorporate some aspect of it in their practices.

For all practical purposes, hypnosis and relaxation induced by someone else are the same. As far as my practice is concerned, the only differentiation between the induction of hypnosis and a progressive relaxation narration is the addition of what is known as 'deepening' to the hypnotic induction.

Deepening, as the term implies, consists of some procedure (I usually count down very slowly from 10 to 1) to increase the depth of the relaxation and results in a much more relaxing experience.

Self-hypnosis is nothing more than relaxing oneself in a planned manner. A common and very effective method of self-hypnosis is simply reciting to oneself a passive progressive relaxation. Like meditation, it is most successful if first done under the guidance of a therapist or a tape.

Techniques of Relaxation

f. Autogenic Training

This method is very similar to the two methods of progressive relaxation described earlier in this book It was developed in Germany in the1930's by Johannes Schultz. Autogenics consists of talking to oneself and thereby focusing one's mind on specific parts of the body and learning to feel sensations (primarily heaviness and warmth) in those parts. Usually the parts selected are hands, arms, feet, or legs. The development of this technique is a relatively slow, tedious procedure requiring many hours of practice. As in the other relaxation techniques, individual differences are great. What comes easy for one person may take a long time for another. Autogenic training is quite popular in western Europe. If you are interested in learning more about autogenic training, I suggest you read the 1959 book by Schultz and Luthe entitled AUTOGENIC TRAINING, CONCENTRATIVE SELF-RELAXATION.

g. Biofeedback

Biofeedback is more accurately a method of measuring and controlling relaxation than it is a relaxation technique in itself. It is mentioned here because it is frequently discussed when relaxation is being considered. Like hypnosis, biofeedback is used for many other purposes than relaxation, but I will only discuss its use in relaxation.

FEEL BETTER! LIVE LONGER! RELAX

Any of the relaxation methods may be used in combination with biofeedback. True to its name, biofeedback is simply a method of 'feeding back' through the eyes or the ears (or both) an objective measurement of the depth of relaxation. Frequently this is done by using a thermometer attached to a finger. As a person relaxes, his/her skin temperature (not body temperature) tends to increase, particularly in the hands. This is because of the increased blood flow resulting from the infinitesimal relaxing of the blood vessels in the skin. A person who is unaware of the power of relaxation will be astonished to find his skin temperature rising by three or four degrees in just a few minutes.

Another biofeedback instrument is the electromyogram which measures muscle tension by measuring electrical activity. Instruments vary as to how they feed back the information but give it either visually or audibly (or both). Muscle tension is a measure of relaxation.

The electroencephalogram is also used as a biofeedback instrument as are other brain-wave measuring devices. The focus on brain waves appears to have declined in recent years, as the early promise of what was called 'alpha biofeedback training' appears not to have been realized.

The Galvanic Skin Response (GSR) is a measure of skin conductance of electricity which in turn is a measure of anxiety. The test is usually made on the hand and this factor

Techniques of Relaxation

has led to the development of some easily used hand held biofeedback instruments. Actually, the GSR is a refinement of the old technique of assessing how sweaty a person's palms are in order to estimate how anxious they are.

Other instruments sometimes used as biofeedback devices are the electrocardiogram (for measuring the rate of heart beat) and the penile plethysmograph (for measuring male sexual arousal).

We are just beginning, as a society, to be aware of the extent to which our so-called 'involuntary' bodily functions can be affected by our minds. Some of these functions are skin temperature, blood pressure, salivation, penile erection, and release of internal bodily fluids such as gastric juices.

h. Other relaxation techniques

The paperback bookshelves in used bookstores contain numerous other techniques for relaxation. These are all variations of the techniques described in this book.

In most relaxation techniques, controlled breathing done according to the directions enhances the beneficial effects of the experience. Deep, slow, rhythmic breathing is relaxing in itself, as is the listening to slow music. According to the theory of SUPERLEARNING listening to music with a beat that is slower than the human heartbeat improves not only the ability to relax but the ability to learn as well. A good source of such music is classical music from the Baroque period, particularly a Vivaldi concerto. It is certainly true that pleasant, slow music played in the background heightens the sensations that accompany deep relaxation. In my practice, I frequently play one of the cassettes of Steve Halpern as a background to either a hypnotic induction or to a passive progressive relaxation narration.

_____

4. Problems Helped by Relaxation

a. Shyness

Shyness is one of the many problems that can be helped through the planned use of relaxation. The anxiety that results in a shy person acting shy in a particular situation can certainly be alleviated by a relaxation technique. I have found that a brief relaxation narration (I use DIMI-TAPE #1— LIVE LONGER, RELAX) listened to just before a public speaking engagement helps reduce my anxiety level and improves my performance. I am sure that other techniques of relaxation would be effective also in handling anticipatory anxiety.

A treatment of the condition of shyness has been developed that is much more than simply a reduction in temporary anxiety. As is the case in all the DIMI-TAPES developed by DIMI PRESS, this is designed for the person in question to use in his/her own self-treatment. The technique uses the psychological procedure of Systematic Desensitization to achieve greater assertiveness. This is part of the instructions on Side A. Side B contains a relaxation narration that fits with Side A and is specifically designed for use in the treatment of shyness.

b. Depression

FEEL BETTER! LIVE LONGER! RELAX

Another tape (DIMI-TAPE #4) that treats a specific disorder is called CONQUER YOUR DEPRESSION. Side A consists of a lecture on the types of depression, causes, and what you can do for the problem. As in all of the DIMI-TAPES it doesn't pretend to substitute for a therapist but if you have a mild problem or if you can't get to a professional, this will help. Side B is a relaxation narration that supplements the message on Side A.

c. Fears

A very effective tape for the overcoming of phobias is called CONQUER YOUR FEARS. As in dealing with the problem of shyness this tape utilizes the technique of Systematic Desensitization. Again, Side A is the lecture and Side B is the relaxation narration. It is DIMI-TAPE #5.

d. Insomnia

Sleeplessness is such a common problem that this tape has turned out to be one of the most popular produced by DIMI PRESS. Side A of DIMI-TAPE #6 contains a lecture focused on what you can do to get a good night's sleep. Side B presents a sleep-inducing narration which is certain to put you to sleep.

e. Cancer

Most people are skeptical when they first hear of the use of relaxation in the treatment of cancer. (I certainly was.) The treatment outlined on the CONTROL YOUR CANCER tape was developed by Dr O. Carl Simonton, a radiation oncologist. Although not yet fully accepted by the cautious medical community, it has been successful many times. The concept is explained in detail on DIMI-TAPE #7. It uses self-analysis, visualization, and other approaches, in addition to relaxation. The tape is expected to be used with the medical treatment of a physician. Side A describes the entire concept and Side B is a lengthy relaxation narration which includes instructions on visualization.

f. Premature Ejaculation

DIMI-TAPE #8 was originally called CONQUER YOUR PREMATURE EJACULATION but is now titled LAST LONGER, ENJOY SEX MORE. Although the problem is that of the man in a sexual relationship, the narration on Side A is designed to be listened to by both partners. This is in keeping with the best thinking by those who specialize in the treatment of sexual disorders. Although not pornographic, the narration is quite explicit on what should be done. Side B is a relaxation narration for the problem and may well be sufficient in itself to solve the problem. In most cases, premature ejaculation is a very easy problem to treat.

g. Weight Control

Although titled WEIGHT CONTROL, most people use DIMI-TAPE #9 for weight loss. In it is stressed the fact that you can control your own weight. Side A is a lecture on controlling your weight and Side B is a relaxation narration including some visualization. The visualization is of yourself and seeing yourself at the weight you want to be. Incidentally, the support of those you live with as you begin a weight loss program is extremely important.

Because of the amount of interest in the problem (and how to solve it), I have included the entire narration in this book.

Following is the script of DIMI-TAPE #9A:

Hello, this is Dick Lutz speaking. I'm going to discuss with you ways in which you can control your weight.

For most people, that means losing first and then maintaining the weight they desire.

Problems Helped by Relaxation

Usually, the extra pounds that people want to lose have built up over many years. Even if they have been acquired fairly quickly (for instance, during a pregnancy), it is best to lose the weight slowly. The more slowly the pounds come off the more likely they are to stay off.

Crash diets or programs are seldom successful in the long run.

You notice that this tape is titled WEIGHT CONTROL, not HOW TO LOSE WEIGHT. That's because it's my conviction that the best approach for you to take is to control your weight just as you control many other things about your life.

Let me talk for a minute about self-control or "freedom of choice' as it might be called. You probably don't realize how much you control many things in your life. Some examples of things that most of us control are the clothes we wear each day, what time we go to bed, and what time we get up. Also you may have partial or complete control of the foods you eat and those you choose not to eat. You choose how to enhance your appearance, when to go to the bathroom, when to brush your teeth, and many other things in your daily life. You choose whether or not to smoke or drink. Some people have the idea that habits like these are beyond their control but that's not true.

EVERY HABIT THAT YOU HAVE HAS BEEN ACQUIRED

AND CAN BE CHANGED!

If you have acquired the habit of eating too much and exercising too little, and thus being overweight, you can change that habit. Or, to say it another way, you can acquire the habit of controlling your weight.

You probably have tried one diet after another over the years without much success. Because of these experiences, and others, you may have decided that you're too 'weak-willed' too control your weight. That's simply not true!

Your will is entirely under your control. It has nothing to do with anything you inherited from your parents.

It has nothing to do with what you've been told by others except as those comments are listened to (and believed) by you.

If you really want to control your weight, you can.

Here are some concrete steps you should follow:

First, listen twice a day to the narration on the other side of this tape. It is designed to help you relax and imagine (or visualize) yourself with your weight under control.

The narration speaks directly to your subconscious and will thus help you to control yourself.

Second, control your food intake. Don't eat between meals, cut down on desserts and sweets. If you're not aware of which foods are high in calories, find out and stay away from them. In my opinion it's best not to count calories exactly as that requires you to spend a lot of your time and energy concentrating on food. I want you to concentrate on self-control, not food. Likewise, I would suggest you weigh only weekly or every other week. Weighing daily puts too much of your attention on the whole process.

Third, exercise regularly. By regularly I mean three times a week or more. Each exercise period should be at least 20 minutes long. If you aren't engaging in an activity that makes you breathe hard you'll have to spend more time than this minimum. Your weight is as much a result of the calories your body burns up as it is of the calories it takes in. Set up an exercise program that is easy to stick to. Don't set impossible goals for yourself. If you haven't been exercising much, it's best to start off slowly. Walk before you run, for instance. The exercise activities you do should be those that result in your working up a sweat and breathing hard.

Exercises like fast walking, jogging, swimming, and bicycle riding are ideal. Activities like calisthenics and weight-lifting are less valuable for your purpose.

Exercising is every bit as important as restricting your food intake. Remember, your weight depends on the balance between the intake and outgo of calories. Both the amount you eat and the amount you exercise are under your complete control.

These are the three main things to do to control your weight. To review, the three are; listen to the narration regularly, control your food intake, and exercise.

Here are some other pointers that will help you to do the three things that are so important.

Get your family's support of your weight control efforts. Those you live with can help in making it possible for you to have the quiet time necessary to listen to your narration.

Your friends and associates, as well as your family, can also be of great help to you in cutting down on your food intake. If someone is serving food to you (for instance, a spouse) it is easy for that person to give you slightly smaller portions at meal time. If you are the person responsible for preparing and serving the food you have even more control over what you eat. Never swallow what you must taste while cooking. Be sure to serve yourself small portions of food.

Those with you at meals can refrain from urging you to take second helpings or eat desserts. If they stay away from these things themselves it will be easier for you.

With exercise, the people around you can not only be

Problems Helped by Relaxation

supportive of your efforts but may be able to exercise with you.

Someone else's participation in what you're doing can certainly make it a lot easier to stick to it.

Let me remind you, though, that control of your weight is up to you, not someone else. Others can help, but you are the only one who can do it.

I suggest that you talk to the people close to you who are in a position to help and ask that they support you. By the way, this definitely includes children who are old enough to understand.

In the actual doing of the three things to gain weight control, here are some suggestions to make them easier:

First, there's the actual listening to the narration. I'd advise you to set a regular time and place for listening to the tape. Figure on listening to it twice a day every day for at least two weeks. By then you will have memorized the narration. The position you're in while relaxing is quite important. The more comfortable you are, the more effective the relaxation/ visualization experience will be.

There are basically three places you can choose in which to relax. If you like, you can lie down, either on a firm mattress or a carpeted floor. Lie flat on your back with a small pillow under your head and a folded blanket or a small pillow under your knees. Arms at your side, but not touching your body. Let your heels be about twelve inches apart. Allow your feet to fall sideways naturally The problem some people have with lying down is that they fall asleep during a relaxation narration. This doesn't do any harm, but it does reduce the impact of the experience and slows down the memorizing of the narration.

Perhaps the most common place in which to relax is a comfortable armchair or reclining chair. Place your arms on the armrests, have your head supported if possible. If in an armchair, have your feet flat on the floor. If in a reclining chair your lower legs will be supported by the chair itself. Don't cross your legs. Every extremity of your body should be supported. In this position you should be so comfortable that you almost feel yourself merging into the chair.

The third position I want to mention is sitting in a straight chair. First, sit upright near the front edge of the seat. Place your feet flat on the floor. If the chair is armless let your arms hang down by your sides and them raise them and let them flop down on your thighs like dead weights. Slide your feet back and forth until the muscles in the front and back are equally relaxed. As nearly as possible the weight of each leg should rest equally on the ball and heel of that foot. Try to arrange yourself so that your head seems balanced on your spinal column and your spinal column seems balanced on your pelvis. Rock your body back and forth feeling the

Problems Helped by Relaxation

---

muscles in your stomach and back until you determine that both sets of muscles are equally relaxed. Do the same with your head while feeling your neck muscles. Now slide back in your seat so that your back touches the chair. Don't lean hard against it. You may now need to readjust your feet. As you can see the key thing in straight chair relaxing is balance. The important thing in other positions is support.

Regardless of the position you're in you can maximize relaxation/visualization by being sure to remove tight clothing or tight belts and shoes. You may want to remove your eyeglasses also. Try to get all your muscles relaxed before starting the relaxation technique itself. You will learn, over time, to relax yourself and to visualize yourself the way you want to be. If possible set aside a quiet, dark place for listening to your narration. Cut down the possibility of distractions. For instance, if you're home alone when you do your relaxing/visualizing you may want to unplug your telephone.

If you make listening to the tape a routine occurrence like brushing your teeth you're more likely to do it.

Concerning controlling your food intake, make it easier for yourself by keeping all food in the kitchen and as inconspicuous as possible even there. Always sit down to eat at the appropriate table. Try not to do anything else but eat at this table and don't eat anywhere else. After serving food to your plate at mealtime, take the serving dishes off the table. The above tips will help you to refrain from eating too much food, but won't keep you from eating what you need. Some other helpful ideas are to not snack between meals (or before bedtime) and to drink lots of water.

About the exercise you do: remember that it is just as important as limiting your food intake. Set up a pattern for yourself so that it will be easy to maintain. If possible, select an exercise (or more than one) that you enjoy. It's probably more important that it be an enjoyable activity than that it be great physical exercise. That way you're more likely to keep it up than if it's drudgery for you.

On the other hand, don't pick an exercise that you like just because you like it. It must be an exercise that burns off calories. Swimming, fast walking, and bicycle riding are three very popular activities that are excellent not only for weight control but for your body and mind generally.

As a rough guideline, I'd suggest that you exercise hard enough to breathe fast at least three times a week. For more specific guidelines consult a book on exercise or your doctor. Of course, if you have a physical handicap or are seriously out of condition you may need to be extra cautious. You be the judge of this, as it's your weight that you're going to control and it's your body.

I"d also like to mention that some of the same tips apply to exercising as to listening to the narration or to eating.

Problems Helped by Relaxation

Create habits that encourage you in the way that you want to go. Exercise (and eat, and listen to your narration) at the same time each day. If the exercise you choose requires special clothing or equipment, get some decent things that function well and make you proud. Reward yourself in some fashion (other than eating, of course) after a good exercise session. An example might be allowing yourself the luxury of a hot bath rather than the quick shower you usually take.

Arrange to do the type, or types, of exercise that you enjoy. Some exercises (running and swimming are examples) can be monotonous. Try turning it into a social activity by finding someone who wants to do the same exercise or join an appropriate club. If running is one exercise you choose, you might wish to participate in some competitions (usually called fun-runs).

You probably don't want to get too competitive, though, because you'll turn what should be fun and beneficial into work. Keep the exercise experience positive for yourself. For example, run or bicycle where it's pleasant and interesting to be, not simply around a monotonous track.

Keeping positive about yourself and your activities, particularly those directed toward weight control, is very important. What I call 'self-talk' is extremely helpful.

Practice telling yourself that you can do things. What I'm talking about on this tape is weight control, but you'll find that keeping a positive attitude helps you in all areas of your life. Get in the habit of talking to yourself internally. Tell yourself over and over that you're good, that you can accomplish whatever it is that you want to accomplish. Assure yourself that everything will turn out well.

Confidence in yourself and your abilities is helpful in self-control, so make efforts to build your self-confidence.

Let yourself feel good about the little things you accomplish. When you lose that first 10 pounds on your weight control program, when you first run a full mile on your exercise program, or whatever goal you achieve, congratulate yourself and reward yourself.

Remember, if you repeatedly tell yourself that you will control your weight, you almost certainly will.

On the other hand, if you do not have a positive attitude toward your program, you will have a tougher time.

I believe that you can succeed in controlling your weight if you believe that you can and if you follow the simple ideas outlined on this tape.

To summarize these ideas again:

First, listen regularly to the narration on the other side of this tape.

Second, limit your eating.

Third, exercise regularly and strenuously enough to burn up the calories you take in.

Do these three things, keep a positive attitude, and you will control your weight.

THANK YOU.

Here is the script of DIMI-TAPE #9B:

Get into position to relax now.

Settle in comfortably.

Now allow your eyes to close and let your thoughts drift to the top of your head, to your scalp. Smooth out the muscles in your scalp. Relax your scalp muscles and let your scalp rest easily on the top of your head.

Now relax your forehead muscles and smooth them out.

Let that relaxation flow down over your eyelids.

Allow the flow to continue down over your cheeks, lips, and chin, letting your whole face become relaxed. Let your jaw muscles relax. Allow your jaw to drop a little if it wants to. Permit your tongue to rest comfortably on the floor of your mouth.

All the muscles of your head are relaxed now. They feel comfortably heavy . . . comfortably heavy.

Now allow the relaxation to flow down your neck and into

your shoulders. Smooth out the muscles of your neck and shoulders. Let them be limp and relaxed. Imagine the muscles as knotted ropes that you untie and let hang loose.

Continue the relaxation in your shoulders, neck, and head while you allow the relaxation to flow down into your upper arms. Relax the muscles of your upper arms, smoothing them out and letting them go.

Now let that relaxation flow into your forearms. Relax the muscles of your forearms. Your arms are feeling comfortably heavy and warm . . . heavy and warm.

Let your hands and fingers relax. Feel the blood flowing comfortably into your fingertips. Your hands and arms are heavy and warm . . . heavy and warm.

FEEL BETTER! LIVE LONGER! RELAX

Keep your head and neck, shoulders and arms relaxed while you let your mind drift to your upper back. Smooth out all the muscles in your upper back and relax them. Allow the muscles to relax down your spine, just letting go.

Let that relaxation come around your body now, smoothing out the muscles around your rib cage. As you breathe, allow your chest to become more and more comfortably relaxed. Feel every breath. Inhale through your nostrils. Take one deep breath, filling up your lungs and then exhaling back out again.

Now you've resumed your regular breathing and it's rhythmic and smooth ... rhythmic and smooth. As you take each breath, let yourself float down.

Problems Helped by Relaxation

Now allow the relaxation to spread down into your abdomen and hips, smoothing out all the muscles.

Let that feeling flow down into your upper legs and let the muscles of your upper legs relax. Smooth them out and let them go.

Now let the relaxation flow into your lower legs, smooth out the muscles in your lower legs causing your legs to be comfortably relaxed. They are heavy and warm . . . heavy and warm.

Finally, the relaxation flows down into your feet, relaxing even the soles of your feet and your toes. Think of your toes getting warm as the blood flows easily to them.

FEEL BETTER! LIVE LONGER! RELAX

Now your whole body from the top of your head to the tips of your toes is relaxed and peaceful. You're comfortable, both inside and out.

With every breath allow your body to let go a little more. Float on down comfortably heavy and relaxed. Be assured that everything is going to be all right.

As you're comfortably relaxing remain awake and aware but very relaxed. Relaxation allows your whole body to have a very deep rest while you're completely awake and aware.

Now that you're completely relaxed I want you to do some visualizing. Imagine yourself as you wish to be. Standing in front of a full-length mirror, looking at yourself. Look at yourself in the mirror. You're slim now and attractive. You're healthy and happy. You have control of your weight and your life.

Just take a while now to enjoy looking at yourself as you will be when your weight is under control. (pause)

In order to become this slim and attractive, healthy and happy, you're going to remember to do a few things.

Don't eat anything except at meal time.

Cut down on fattening foods and drinks.

Drink lots of water.

Now let yourself relax even deeper and think about how

you're going to burn up those calories.

Visualize a flame and think of those calories burning up.

During each week you're exercising at least three times in order to burn up those calories.

The exercise is enjoyable. It not only helps you to control your weight but it makes you feel good, too.

Again, visualize yourself as you will look when your weight is under control.

You're slim and attractive. You're healthy and happy.

Relax again now.

Problems Helped by Relaxation

You will do these relaxation/visualization sessions twice a day and you will control your weight.

Just relax for awhile more. (pause)

I want you to feel free to continue to relax as long as you wish or, if you're ready, allow yourself to become aware of your surroundings, and allow your eyes to open while remaining relaxed, feeling good, and refreshed.

This is the end of the narration.

h. Stop Smoking

FEEL BETTER! LIVE LONGER! RELAX

The number of people who still smoke even after all the research showing the dangerousness of it is astounding. Most smokers have tried to quit, but unfortunately nicotine addiction is among the hardest of the addictions to cure. Like other similar problems, it is really both a habit and an addiction.

Whatever you call it, the most important factor in the success of quitting is the motivation of the person involved. It's not a question of whether your doctor, your spouse, or someone else has told you that you should quit, but whether YOU really want to quit.

If you have the personal desire to quit, it certainly can be accomplished, either by relaxation/hypnosis or by another technique. DIMI-TAPE #10, STOP SMOKING, produced by DIMI PRESS, consists of a lecture on the problem on Side A and a relaxation narration directed to the problem on Side B. This relaxation narration contains the 'deepening' which is usually associated with hypnosis. This increases its effectiveness.

Here is the script of DIMI-TAPE #10A:

This is Dick Lutz speaking.

Problems Helped by Relaxation

I'm going to talk with you about ways in which you can stop smoking.

Since you're listening to this tape I think it's safe for me to assume that smoking cigarettes (and/or cigars or pipes) is a habit you have and wish to change. Smoking is a habit which you have picked up in your life. Every habit that you have has been acquired and can be changed. The habits you have collected over your lifetime are yours and they are under your control. If you really want to change your habit you can. This is an important point. The degree of your motivation makes all the difference. If you really want to quit, you can. It doesn't matter what prompts you. Your doctor may have told you to quit or face an early death. The important people in your life may be bugging you to quit. You may be tired of coughing and having bronchitis frequently. You may look forward to being able to smell and taste better. You may be tired of replacing clothes that aren't worn out but have burn holes in them. Whatever your reason, it is important that you really desire to quit - totally and permanently.

Remember, you are in control of your life and if you want to change one of your habits you certainly can. Self-control is something you exercise a lot, probably more than you realize. After all you are the one who controls what and how much you eat, what you wear, how you enhance your appearance, and when you brush your teeth. You control many, many things in your life and you can control your smoking, too.

You may have tried to quit smoking and been unable to. This is frustrating and it may have resulted in your feeling that you don't have the will to quit. THAT'S NOT TRUE! Your will is entirely under your control. It has nothing to do with anything that you inherited from your parents. It has nothing to do with what you have been told by others, except as you listen to and (perhaps) believe those comments. As are so many other things in your life, your will is completely under your control. If you sincerely will yourself to stop smoking, you'll stop.

Here are some concrete steps you can take to make the process easier:

First, listen twice a day to the narration on the reverse side of this tape. It helps you relax and visualize your self having stopped smoking. It reminds you of the many benefits you'll receive from changing the habit of smoking to the habit of not smoking. The suggestions on the tape speak directly to your subconscious mind and help you in the process of self-control. I would suggest listening to the tape twice daily for awhile.

Second, substitute another habit for the habit of smoking. If you analyze your smoking you'll probably find that you smoke at certain predictable times such as after meals. Let me suggest that you substitute a harmless, or perhaps even

---

beneficial, habit instead. Taking a walk, drinking a glass of water, eating raisins, or chewing a toothpick, are all habits that have been used by many, many people who are now ex-smokers. If none of these habits appeal to you, why don't you invent one of your own?

Third, exercise regularly. By regularly I mean at least three times a week. Each exercise period should be at least twenty minutes long. If you do not engage in an activity that makes you sweat and breathe hard, you'll have to spend even more time than this minimum. One of the main reasons for stopping smoking is so that you'll feel, and be, healthier. Exercise can only add to this healthy feeling. Also, of course, it gives you an added activity to engage in.

Although it will vary for different individuals the single most important thing to do for most people is to listen regularly to the relaxation narration on the tape. This will back up, or reinforce (to use the technical term), your own resolution to stop smoking.

By the way, if you haven't totally resolved to quit I'd advise your taking a closer look at your smoking habit and whether or not you want to change it. It's not impossible to quit smoking if you have mixed feelings about the whole process, but it's certainly much easier to quit if you strongly want to quit.

Let me summarize what I've said so far regarding actual

things to do while quitting.

One, listen regularly to the relaxation narration.

Two, substitute a positive habit for your cigarette habit, and,

Three, exercise.

One of the questions that you have to decide when stopping smoking is exactly how or when do you do it. Many people taper off with or without the aid of mechanical devices, such as special filters. Probably most people quit cold turkey. They just stop. If you wish, you can throw away your cigarettes right now while listening to this tape and never smoke again.

I'd like to discuss another idea that has been quite successful for many people, particularly those with breathing problems that are made worse by smoking. This involves setting a day to stop smoking probably less than a week after the decision is made and then, the day before you've decided to stop, smoke twice as much as you're used to and smoke a brand that you don't like (preferably one that's too strong for your taste). This concept takes advantage of what's called 'aversive conditioning'. It leaves you with a bad recollection of smoking and thus even less likely than otherwise to return to the habit.

Problems Helped by Relaxation

Whichever way you choose to quit, make a decision and stick to it. It may be that you've already quit and are listening to this tape to help strengthen your resolve. If so, I want to compliment you on quitting and urge you to listen to the relaxation narration right away. Also, begin exercising if you're not already and substitute something for the cigarette you used to smoke.

At this point I'd like to mention some other tips. If you can possibly get the support of those around you in your effort it will be very helpful. For instance, if your spouse smokes I would suggest asking him or her to quit with you or, at least, not smoke in your presence. Your colleagues at school or job can also be asked to support you in your undertaking. The less temptation you have to undergo, the easier the whole process of quitting smoking will be for you. The people around you can also be very helpful in assisting you with your exercise routine. Perhaps you can find someone who will run or bike with you and thus make it more fun.

I would caution you against trying to tackle another major problem at the same time as you stop smoking. Unless you are dangerously overweight, I don't think it's advisable to try to lose a large amount of weight at the same time as you stop smoking. For the same reasons, I would advise against your stopping smoking at the same time as you're undergoing a divorce, have recently lost your job, are in the process of making a major move, or are going through some other major crisis. The reason I advise against tackling two major personal problems at once is because that only makes it harder to succeed. Also, some people can go into a depression from trying to handle too many personal problems at once. Be good to yourself is one of the first rules of living.

I'd like to talk about the problem so many people worry about when they start a stop smoking program. That is a fear that they will gain weight. This can happen if an ex-smoker lets himself/herself eat more to substitute for smoking. However, if you consciously substitute something without calories, like water or toothpicks, and avoid increasing your food intake you will NOT gain weight. With the exercising I advocate you will probably will lose, not gain, as you stop smoking.

The first of the steps to take in stopping smoking is to listen to the narration on the other side of this tape. I'd advise you to set a regular time and place for listening to the tape. Figure on listening to it twice a day every day for at least two weeks. After that, you may gradually memorize the narration.

The position you're in while relaxing is quite important. The more comfortable you are, the more effective the relaxation/visualization experience will be. There are basically three places you can choose in which to relax. If you like, you can lie down— either on a firm mattress or on a carpeted floor. Lie flat on your back with a small pillow under your head and, perhaps, a folded blanket or small pillow under your knees.

Problems Helped by Relaxation

Arms at your side but not touching your body. Let your heels be about twelve inches apart and allow your feet to fall sideways naturally. The problem some people have with lying down is that they will fall asleep during their relaxation narration. This doesn't do any harm but it does reduce the impact of the visualization experience and slows down the memorizing of the narration.

Perhaps the most common place in which to relax is a comfortable armchair or reclining chair. Place your arms on the armrests. Have your head supported if possible. If in an armchair, have your feet flat on the floor. If in a reclining chair, your lower legs and feet will be supported by the chair. Don't cross your legs. Every extremity of your body should be supported. In this position you should be so comfortable that you almost feel yourself merging into the chair.

Another position for relaxation is in a straight chair. In a straight chair the most important thing is balance, rather than support. Think of a string holding your head straight up. Balance your head on your spinal column and your spinal column on your pelvis. If there are no armrests on your chair, let your arms rest loosely on your thighs. If you relax at work this may be the most practical position for you.

Regardless of the position you're in, you can maximize the relaxation/visualization by being sure to loosen or remove tight clothing or tight belts and shoes. You may want to take off your glasses. Try to get all your muscles relaxed before starting the relaxation technique itself. You will learn, over time, to relax yourself and to visualize yourself the way you want to be. If possible set aside a quiet, dark place for listening to your narration. Cut down the possibility of distractions. For instance, if you're home alone at the time you do your relaxing and visualizing you may wish to unplug your telephone. If you make listening to the tape a routine occurrence in your life, like brushing your teeth, you're more likely to do it.

Substituting something for a cigarette is important to your stopping smoking. Think of a substitute that is beneficial or, at least, harmless and something that is available to you wherever you smoke. For example, you may have a job that involves attending a lot of meetings and that's one place you smoke. When you stop smoking you might find it easier to chew gum in meetings rather than to eat fruit. Pick what's best for you. Use different substitutes at different times. Make the whole process as easy for yourself as possible. Don't play games by tempting yourself. If possible, eliminate smoking completely from your environment. Almost always, relatives, friends, and work associates will help you to quit smoking if you just ask them. Don't keep cigarettes or ashtrays in your living place or work place. Ask people who call on you not to smoke. A THANK YOU FOR NOT SMOKING sign will convey the message to your visitors without calling attention to the point.

A few more comments about exercising. This is a very

important aspect of the change you're undergoing. Create habits that encourage you to exercise. Have a positive attitude about it. Try to make it fun not work. Exercise at the same time each day if you can. If the exercise you select requires special clothing or equipment get some decent things that function well and make yourself proud. Reward yourself in some fashion after a good exercise session. An example might be allowing yourself the luxury of a hot bath rather than the quick shower you usually take. You might consider making the exercise activity into a social one by finding someone who wants to do the same thing. It may be easier to keep your motivation this way. Make the exercise experience pleasant for yourself. For example, if the exercise you choose is walking, running, or bicycling pick an area that's interesting to be in rather than just going around on a monotonous track.

Another practice that can be very beneficial to you, both as you stop smoking and in your life generally is developing the habit of self-talk. Tell yourself (probably speaking just in your mind) that you CAN do things. Get in the habit of talking to yourself internally, telling yourself that you're good - that you can stop smoking - that you can accomplish whatever it is that you want to accomplish. Assure yourself that everything will turn out well. Confidence in yourself and your abilities is helpful in self-control so make efforts to build your self-confidence. Let yourself feel good about the little things you accomplish. When you go without smoking for a day, a week, or a month or first run a full mile on your exercise program— congratulate yourself— reward yourself. Remember, if you repeatedly tell yourself that you WILL stop smoking you're almost certain to succeed. On the other hand if you do not have a positive attitude toward your program you will have a tougher time.

I believe that you can stop smoking if you believe that you can and if you follow the simple ideas outlined on this tape. To summarize the main ideas again:

One, listen regularly to the narration on the reverse of this tape.

Two, substitute a habit of your choice for the habit of smoking a cigarette.

Three, exercise regularly.

Do these three things, keep a positive attitude, and you WILL stop smoking.

If you have any need to, feel free to get in touch with me. My name is Dick Lutz and you can write me at P.O. Box 3363, Salem, Oregon 97302.

Thank you.

Here is the script of DIMI-TAPE #10B:

Problems Helped by Relaxation

Get into a comfortable position now and adjust the volume on your tape recorder so that it's comfortable for you. Just sit back and relax.

Now, let your mind travel to the top of your head. Think about the muscles on the top of your head. Think about how relaxed they are. How loose and comfortable. It's like your scalp is just resting quietly on the top of your head. (pause)

Now the relaxation flows down over you forehead. Relaxing the muscles of your forehead. Just smoothing out your forehead. (pause)

Now the relaxation flows down over your eyelids, closing your eyes if you like. Relaxing all your facial muscles. Your cheeks relax, your chin, your lips, even your tongue is resting quietly on the floor of your mouth. You're more and more comfortable in your chair now. The tension of the day is leaving your body. (pause)

Now the relaxation flows right down the back of your neck and into the muscles of your upper back, relaxing those muscles, letting them be free. It's like the muscles of your upper back are knotted ropes that you untie and let hang loose. (pause)

Now the relaxation flows out over your shoulders and

down into the muscles of your upper arms. Think about the muscles of your upper arms becoming relaxed, loose, and free. (pause)

Now allow the relaxation to flow on down into the muscles of your lower arms. Relaxing the muscles of your lower arms. (pause)

Now allow the relaxation to flow down into your hands. Relaxing all the muscles of your hands and fingers. The relaxation flows comfortably into your fingertips. (pause)

Now your hands and arms are completely relaxed. They're heavy and warm . . . heavy and warm. (pause)

Now return in your mind to the relaxed muscles of your upper back and just let the relaxation flow straight down your back, right down your spine. Into the muscles of your lower back. The muscles of your lower back are very relaxed now, they're loose and limp. (pause)

Now the relaxation flows around your body, into the muscles over your rib cage. Relaxing those muscles, letting them be loose. (pause)

Your breathing is normal now. It's rhythmic and smooth . . . rhythmic and smooth. (pause)

Now the relaxation flows right down your body into the

---

muscles of your abdomen and hips, relaxing all the muscles of your abdomen and hips. You're very comfortable in your chair. (pause)

Now the relaxation flows down into the muscles of your upper legs, relaxing the muscles of your upper legs. Letting them be loose. (pause)

Now the relaxation flows down further into the muscles of your lower legs, relaxing the muscles of your lower legs. Letting them be loose and limp. (pause)

Now the relaxation flows down into your feet, relaxing all the muscles of your feet and your toes. Even the soles of your feet are relaxed now. You feel the relaxation flowing comfortably into your toes. (pause)

Your feet and legs are completely relaxed now. They're heavy and warm. . . heavy and warm. (pause)

You're completely relaxed now from the top of your head to the tips of your toes. You feel as if you're floating on a cloud and at the same time you're comfortably heavy. (pause)

Now that you're so completely relaxed I want you to do some visualizing, some imagining of seeing yourself in a comfortable place. Perhaps it's some place you were once in. It's pleasant here. You feel warm and comfortable. There's nothing around to bother you. It's just nice. You feel good.

FEEL BETTER! LIVE LONGER! RELAX

You are proud that you've stopped smoking. Your breathing is becoming more and more clear. You're healthier and happier. Your food tastes better. You have control over your life. You are improving your health and increasing your happiness by continuing to refrain from smoking. When you want a cigarette you'll substitute something else instead. You'll exercise at least three times a week and exercise will help you feel good. You will listen to this tape twice a day and eventually memorize it. (pause)

Now as you continue to feel relaxed I want you to allow yourself to relax even more as I gradually count down from ten to one. You will relax more deeply with each number I count. Until, at the count of ONE, you will be very deeply relaxed.

Now, at TEN you are comfortably relaxed, but at NINE and EIGHT you are more relaxed. Your mind is relaxed as well as your body. At SEVEN and SIX you're more and more relaxed. At FIVE and FOUR you're very relaxed. At THREE and TWO you're very, very relaxed.

And at ONE, you're extremely relaxed. Very, very, very deeply relaxed now. (pause)

Now once again see yourself in your comfortable place. Perhaps it's someplace you were once in. It's pleasant here. You feel warm and comfortable. There's nothing around to bother you. It's just nice. You feel good. You are proud that you've stopped smoking. Your breathing is becoming more and more clear. You're healthier and happier. Your food tastes better. You have control over your life. You are improving your health and increasing your happiness by continuing to refrain from smoking. When you want a cigarette you'll substitute something else instead. You'll exercise at least three times a week and exercise will help you feel good. You will listen to this tape twice a day and eventually memorize it.

Just stay in that place for a few moments, enjoying yourself. (pause)

Now as I gradually count upwards from one to ten, you will come awake. As you come awake you will be alert, refreshed, feel good and realize that you are in control of your life.

At ONE you're still deeply relaxed, but at TWO and THREE you're stirring internally. At FOUR and FIVE you're coming awake a bit more. At SIX and SEVEN your muscles are moving, your eyelids may be fluttering. At EIGHT and NINE you're coming awake further and at TEN you're completely awake.

You now feel so good.

---

i. Others

DIMI PRESS presently makes no other tapes that deal with psychological problems but that doesn't mean that relaxation can't be used for a variety of other disorders. Among the conditions that can be appropriately treated by the use of relaxation are headaches, muscle spasms, muscle aches and pain, pain in general, stomach upsets, asthma, allergies, skin disorders, warts, female breast underdevelopment, alcoholism, drug addiction, impotence, and high blood pressure. I am sure that there are other conditions that can be alleviated through the use of relaxation.

AFTERWORD

In this book I have attempted to present you with a review of those techniques of relaxation with which I am familiar. If you find others that are helpful to you by all means use them. My belief is that relaxation is very beneficial to virtually everyone. But the specific technique that is most helpful to any individual can only be determined by that individual.

You are urged to record the tape of your choice for your own use if you wish to, but remember that both the tapes and the scripts are copyrighted and cannot be sold.

You are welcome to order any of the tapes I make. Many people prefer someone else's voice on tape to their own. It is frequently difficult for the novice to achieve the correct speed (or pacing) for maximum effect. The order form at the back of this book lists all the tapes in this book as well as some others produced by DIMI PRESS. A personalized narration can also be ordered.

BIBLIOGRAPHY

Barber, Theodore X. and Wilson, Sheryl C. "The Fantasy-Prone Personality: Implication for Understanding Imagery, Hypnosis, and Parapsychological Phenomena." IMAGERY: CURRENT THEORY, RESEARCH, AND APPLICATIONS, edited by Anees A. Sheikh.   New York: John Wiley & Sons,1983.

Benson, Dr. Herbert. THE RELAXATION RESPONSE. New York: William Morrow,1975.

Blanchard, Edward B. and Epstein, Leonard H.   A BIO-FEEDBACK PRIMER. Reading, Massachusetts: Addison-Wesley,1978.

Bloomfield, Dr. Harold H.; Cain, Michael Peter; Jaffe, Dennis T.; and Kory, Robert B. TM, DISCOVERING INNER ENERGY AND OVERCOMING STRESS. New York: Dell,1975.

Denniston, Denise and McWilliams,Peter. THE TM BOOK. New York: Warner Books,1975.

Derogatis, Dr. Leonard R. "Self-report Measures of Stress." In HANDBOOK OF STRESS. Edited by Leo Goldberger and Shlomo Breznitz. New York: The Free Press,1982.

Edmonston, William E. HYPNOSIS AND RELAXATION. New York: Wiley,1981.

Friedman, Dr. Meyer, and Rosenman, Dr. Ray H. TYPE A BEHAVIOR AND YOUR HEART. New York: Knopf, 1974.

Harris, Louis. INSIDE AMERICA. New York: Vintage,1987.

Jacobson, Dr. Edmund. PROGRESSIVE RELAXATION. Chicago: University of Chicago Press,1929.

Jacobson, Dr. Edmund. YOU MUST RELAX. 5th Edition, New York: McGraw-Hill, 1978.

LeShan, Lawrence. HOW TO MEDITATE. 6th Printing, New York: Bantam Books, 1975.

Mason, L. John. GUIDE TO STRESS REDUCTION. Culver City, California: Peace Press,1980.

Ostrander, Sheila; Ostrander, Nancy; and Schroeder, Lynn. SUPERLEARNING. 5th Printing, New York: Dell Publishing, 1981.

Pelletier, Kenneth R. MIND AS HEALER, MIND AS SLAYER. New York: Dell,1977.

Samuels, Dr. Mike and Samuels, Nancy. SEEING WITH THE MIND'S EYE, THE HISTORY, TECHNIQUES AND USES OF VISUALIZATION. New York: Random House,1975.

Schultz, Dr. J., and W. Luthe. AUTOGENIC TRAINING: A PSYCHOPHYSIOLOGIC APPROACH IN PSYCHOTHER-APY. New York: Grune and Stratton, 1959.

Selye, Dr. Hans. STRESS WITHOUT DISTRESS. New York: Lippincott   and Crowell,1974.

Simonton, Dr. O. Carl; Matthews-Simonton, Stephanie; and Creighton, James. GETTING WELL AGAIN. Los Angeles: J.P. Tarcher, Inc., 1978.

INDEX

133

DIMI PRESS PRODUCTS FOR YOU

DIMI-TAPES are $9.95 each. We have the following 16 titles:

#1- LIVE LONGER, RELAX
#2-ACTIVE RELAXATION
#3-CONQUER YOUR SHYNESS
 #4-CONQUER YOUR DEPRESSION
#5-CONQUER YOUR FEARS
#6-CONQUER YOUR INSOMNIA
#7-CONTROL YOUR CANCER
#8-LAST LONGER, ENJOY SEX MORE
      (re PREMATURE EJACULATION)
#9-WEIGHT CONTROL
 #10-STOP SMOKING
#11-LIVE LONGER, RELAX(Female voice)
#12-ACTIVE RELAXATION(Femalevoice)
#13-UNWIND WHILE DRIVING
#14-RELAX AWHILE
#15-RELAX ON THE BEACH/
      RELAX IN A MEADOW
#16-HOW TO MEDITATE

GUIDE TO RELAXATION is a six-cassette album for $49.95.

FEEL BETTER! LIVE LONGER! RELAX is this book and is #9.95.

ORDER FORM

DIMI-TAPE # _____x$9.95 = _____

GUIDE TO RELAXATION _____x49.95 = _____

FEEL BETTER!
LIVE LONGER!
RELAX _____x9.95 = _____

             Postage & handling _____2.00

                        TOTAL _____

___Check enclosed

              < Acct.#_____

__VISA/MC   < Exp. date_____

             Signature_____

Name_____

Address _____

City/State/Zip _____

Phone(____)_____

        Send to: DIMI PRESS
            PO BOX 3363
           Salem, OR 97302

Or call:(503)364-7698

ORDER FORM

DIMI-TAPE # _____x$9.95 = _____

GUIDE TO RELAXATION _____x49.95 = _____

FEEL BETTER!
LIVE LONGER!
RELAX _____x9.95 = _____

           Postage & handling _____ 2.00

                TOTAL _____

___Check enclosed
             ╱ Acct.#_____
__VISA/MC ╱ Exp. date_____

           Signature_____
Name_____

Address _____

City/State/Zip _____

Phone(_____)_____
       Send to: DIMI PRESS
             PO BOX 3363
             Salem, OR 97302
Or call:(503)364-7698